A History of the

Jacob Sheep

by Araminta Aldington

Published in 1989

for

The Jacob Sheep Society

Registered with the Charity Commissioners
No. 259858

by

Geerings of Ashford Ltd.,

*The Publishers are kindly making a donation
to
The Jacob Sheep Society
for each book sold*

JACOB SHEEP SOCIETY

Amendments to original copy

Errata.	Page 10	Pl. II Egyptian 1800 B.C.
	33	Below WAND, "Small change" not charge
	39	70th line "sock lamb" not "stock"
	44	5th para "beggar woman"
	55	Above race horse "The Earl of Halifax"
	64	4th line "sock lamb" not "stock"
	80	5th para. "Persia in 1920".
	96	6th line. "visit to Scotland, painted a flock...."
	101	No. 10 "Miss Barbara Batt"
	107	Ogilvy - with huge apologies to our Patron
	116	Add:- "LII Copyright Trustees of the National Museums of Scotland"

© The Lady Aldington

ISBN 0 9513042 5 9

Designed and printed by Geerings of Ashford Ltd., Cobbs Wood House, Ashford, Kent

Be careful to know your own sheep
and take good care of your flocks;
for possessions do not last for ever.

Proverbs 27 v. 23
The New English Bible

Message from the author

This appreciation of the Jacob or Piebald Sheep is inevitably fragmented, due to the vast chronological range involved.

It is hoped that some of these disconnected strands may be found to be of sufficient interest to be used by a future researcher, to work a larger more complete tapestry giving a fuller picture of this unique breed of sheep.

Araminta Aldington

The first Official History of the Jacob Sheep would not have been possible without the help of the following Charitable Trusts and individuals who have so generously contributed to its research.

The William Scott Abbott Trust
Sir John and Lady Amory Charitable Trust
The Ernest Cook Trust
The Curzonia Charitable Trust Fund
The Edmund de Rothschild Charitable Trust
The Leopold de Rothschild Charitable Trust
The Duke of Devonshire's Trust
The Dulverton Trust
The Elmgrant Trust
The Fox Memorial Trust
The Gilchrist Educational Trust
Mrs. M. M. Gill's Charitable Trust
The Godinton Charitable Trust
The Jane Hodge Foundation
The JR & SR (1977) Charitable Trust
Mr. J. Lyons
The M.F.H. Charitable Trust
The MacRoberts Trusts
The Lord & Lady Margadale Charitable Trusts
The Hon. Mary Morrison D.B.E. Charitable Trust
The Esme Mitchell Trust
Mrs. Partridge
The Rayne Foundation
Mrs. D. M. Rettie
The A. F. Wallace Charity Trust
Major Michael T. Wills Trust
Anon.

Many kind people have, over the years, helped me collect and collate the fascinating material for this book. It would be impossible to name them all as it has been a gradual, but loving, task. Particular thanks should go to the late Mr. Heatley Noble without who's 'spade work' and effort very little of the contents of this book would have been possible. (See p. 35)

My lasting thanks must go to Sally Potter who's help with the last frantic rush to the publisher in time for the Jacob Sheep Society's 20th Birthday in 1989 has been invaluable.

Mr. Robert Geering of Ashford, has very kindly offered to publish this work, for which the Jacob Sheep Society is extremely grateful.

Contents

The Bible Story   7

Evidence of Pied Sheep   11

The Park Sheep Society   29

The Flocks of Jacob Sheep in the British Isles   35

Information required please   94

The Epilogue   95

Pictorial Evidence   96

The First Hundred Members   101

Council of the Jacob Sheep Society 1989   107

Members of the Jacob Sheep Society   108

Notes on illustrations   115

Dedicated to Ebony
The first ever champion Jacob Sheep
Exhibited by the author at the 1971 Royal Show

The Bible Story

The Jacob sheep takes its name from the story told in the Old Testament Book of Genesis of how Jacob became a selective breeder of pied sheep.

Jacob, the second son of Isaac and Rebecca, had dishonestly obtained his father's blessing intended for his elder son Esau. This had provoked such rage in Esau that he had threatened to kill his brother. Both Isaac and Rebecca decided it would be best if Jacob went on a visit to his uncle Laban, Rebecca's brother, 'until your brother's fury turns away'.

Esau

So Jacob travelled north from Beersheba to Paddan-aram, 'The Plain of Aram'. It was here that Abraham had sent his son Isaac to find a wife, and now in turn Isaac was sending his son on the same mission. This would have involved a journey of some one thousand kilometres along the ancient caravan route to Mesopotamia via the Sea of Galilee, Damascus, Aleppo and Northern Syria.

Here, at a watering place he enquired of the local shepherds if they knew his uncle Laban and if all was well with him. They answered, "It is well; and see, Rachel his daughter is coming with the sheep!"

Jacob was then warmly welcomed by Laban, and some time later fell in love with Laban's daughter, Rachel, and wished to marry her. He was now tending Laban's flocks but, being a kinsman, had not been paid; it was agreed that in order to marry Rachel he would work unpaid for seven years 'and they seemed to him but a few days because of the love he had for her'. However, Laban did not keep his promise because he was determined that Jacob should marry Leah his eldest daughter, whose 'eyes were weak' whereas 'Rachel was beautiful and lovely'. At the end of the agreed time Jacob was made to work, unpaid, for a further seven years and only then did Laban give 'him his daughter Rachel to wife'.

After Jacob and Rachel's son Joseph was born 'Jacob said to Laban, "Send me away, that I may go to my own home and country" '; not wanting Jacob and his young family to leave Paddan-aram, Laban offered to pay Jacob any wage whatsoever. 'Jacob said, "You shall not give me anything; if you will do this for me, I will again feed your flock and keep it: let me pass through all your flock today, removing from it every speckled and spotted sheep and every black lamb, and the spotted and speckled among the goats; and such shall be my wages. So my honesty will answer for me later, when you come to look into my wages with you. Every one that is not speckled and spotted among the goats, and black among the lambs, if found with me, shall be counted stolen" '.

Laban agreed to this, but that same day he gave his sons the black lambs promised to Jacob and removed them a 'distance of three days' journey'.

Jacob, left with the rest of Laban's flock, took them to a watering place and, having peeled off strips from fresh poplar, almond and plane saplings, stuck them in the ground where the flocks came to drink. According to this folklore, the ewes having been tupped by the ram before the rods 'brought forth striped, speckled and spotted' lambs. These Jacob

I. Sicilian c.600 B.C.

Wives on Camels

bred from by using the spotted and black older stock and keeping them 'apart, and did not put them with Laban's flock. Whenever the stronger of the flock were breeding, Jacob laid the rods in the runnels before the eyes of the flock, that they might breed among the rods, but for the feebler of the flock he did not lay them there; so the feebler were Laban's, and the stronger Jacob's. Thus the man grew exceedingly rich, and had large flocks, maidservants and menservants, and camels and asses'.

God then said to Jacob in a dream, ' "Now arise, go forth from this land, and return to the land of your birth" Jacob arose, and set his sons and his wives on camels; and he drove away all his cattle, all his livestock. . . . which he had acquired in Paddan-aram, to go to the land of Canaan to his father Isaac. . . . And Jacob outwitted Laban the Aramean, in that he did not tell him that he intended to flee. He fled with all that he had, and arose and crossed the Euphrates, and set his face towards the hill country of Gilead'.

The Old Testament consists of a collection of tales handed down through the generations between the 12th and the 2nd Century B.C., so it is interesting to read the various translations of Genesis 30 verse 32 which have been used over the centuries:-

Wycliffe (1350-1380) uses the words:-

'I shal feede and kepe thi beestis. Turne abowt alle thi flockis, and seuer [sever] alle thi speckid sheep, and with speckyd flese, and what euere [ever] zolow [yellow], and speckid, and dyuerse colourid were, as wel in sheep as in geyt [goats] shal be my mede [reward].'

In 1530 William Tyndale in his version of 'The fyrst boke of Moses, called Genesis' quoted:-

'I will go aboute all thy shepe this daye, and separate fro all the shepe that are spotted and of dyuerse colours, and all blacke shepe amonge the lambes and the partie and spotted amonge the kyddes: And then such shal be my rewarde.'

The Geneva Bible was immensely popular, from 1560-1616 no year passed without a new edition; in 1599 the verse we are interested in reads:

'I will passe through all they flocks this day and separate from them all the sheppe with little spots and great spots.'

At the command of King James I, the Authorized Version was begun in 1607 and published in 1611; verse 32 reads:-

'I will pass through all they flock to day, removing from thence all the speckled and spotted cattle, and all the brown cattle among the sheep.'

Verse 8 reads:-

'The speckled shall be the wages; then all the cattle bare speckled: and if he said thus, the ringstraked shall be they hire; then bare all the cattle ringstraked.'

The Revised Standard Version from which 'The Bible Story' is taken was issued between 1946 and 1952. The words used in v.32 are:-

'every speckled and spotted one, and every black one among the sheep,'

In 1966 the Old Testament had been translated for the New English Bible, published in full in 1970. The relevant passage uses the words:-

'Today I will go over your flocks and pick out from them every spotted and brindled sheep and every black lamb.'

Note: The Hebrew version mentioned in the foot note has been included.

It is worth while to remember that Jacob said 'Every one that is not speckled and spotted among the goats and black among the lambs, if found with me, shall be counted stolen'. Surely this must refer to the special preference given to white lambs in the Lord's command to Moses for the Children of Israel (Numbers 28 vv 3, 9 and 11): ' "You shall say to them, this is the offering by fire which you shall offer to the Lord: two male lambs a year old without blemish. . . . On the sabbath day two male lambs a year old without blemish. . . . At the beginnings of your months. . . . two young bulls, one ram, seven male lambs a year old without blemish" '. The Authorised Version uses the words 'without spot'. Even more explicit is the description given in The New Testament by St. Peter (I Peter I v 19) of the perfect lamb 'a lamb without blemish or spot'. This would seem to indicate that white lambs had to be used for sacrifice; it may be that they were far fewer and more difficult to breed.

To return to the story of Jacob, now in his old age. Unbeknownst to him, his son Joseph had become governor of Egypt. Hearing that it was possible to buy corn in Egypt, Jacob sent his sons to buy some as there had been a seven year famine 'in all lands'. Face to face with their brother, whom they had sold as a child to a caravan of traders carrying gum, balm and myrrh to Egypt, they did not recognise him, but he recognised them and after giving them a spell in prison, he persuaded his brothers to fetch their father, saying ' "Make haste and go up to my father and say to him, 'Thus says your son Joseph, God has made me lord of all Egypt; come down to me, do not tarry; you shall dwell in the land of Goshen, and you shall be near me, you and your children and your children's children, and your flocks, your herds, and all that you have'." "

Jacob's sheep thus travelled from Palestine to Egypt and so perhaps on to Spain via the coast of North Africa and Morocco (See p. 23 X).

II. Sicilian c.600 B.C.

Evidence Of Pied Sheep

Spotted sheep are probably the oldest breed of sheep in the world. Their markings provided camouflage to protect them in their original feral state from marauding mountain lions and the like. To this day, to see a closely packed flock of Jacobs moving across a field is to be reminded of this fact; a 20th Century shepherd once remarked, 'They travel more like deer than sheep', which is very true. Oddly enough this action can best be seen in an 1800 B.C. Egyptian wall painting where two of the sheep are spotted, have Nubian goat-like ears and carry the corkscrew horns we will hear more of later. (See MONTREAL).

Professor Paul Link of Rehovot in Israel maintains that in ancient days two distinct types of spotted sheep were bred, the domestic and the fighting rams with forward growing horns used to protect the nomadic flocks.

As stories from the Bible date from the 12th to the 2nd Century B.C. it is worth looking at the wonderful animal creations made in pure gold by the Scythians during the 1,000 years before Our Lord. The world of the migrant Scythians stretched through the grasslands of Siberia, both east and west, to cover the enormous area from China to Greece and as far south as Iran and Egypt. A superb golden pectoral (ornate neck piece) excavated in Siberia, now in the Gold Rooms of the State Hermitage Museum, Leningrad, consists of two rows of finely delineated animals. The top row are domestic, the outside row are imaginary creatures such as winged dragons. Two sheep are shown in great detail, one being milked, the other grazing; both are long tailed, small eared, two horned and without the 'peculiar elevation or arching of the nasal bones seen in some eastern races' (See p. 19). Unfortunately there is no evidence of the colour of their short curly fleeces.

These pied sheep seem to have inspired artists from many different periods and countries to commit very detailed likenesses to paper, canvas or vessels for their owners, thereby giving a creative record to be researched. It would seem that highly talented artists were sometimes commissioned to depict these prized animals, much as today the photographer would be asked to take a picture.

There is also good evidence of the existence of spotted sheep around the Mediterranean, Persia and Arabia in the centuries leading up to the Birth of Christ.

In Sicily, during the Corinthian Period (c.600 B.C.), several terracotta vessels were fashioned in the form of rams carefully dotted with spots, usually two horned with small ears.

The well fed animal seen on page eight did duty as a water or wine vessel, the spouts springing from the back and tail where both rims are missing; 9″ long, the body is painted with dark brown dappling.

The domesticated ram, described as a 'goat', dates from the first half of the 1st Century B.C. and was painted on a glazed terracotta vessel in Assyria [Iraq]. This active animal, its long tail a clue to it being a direct ancestor of the present day Jacob is two-horned, small eared and wearing a head collar; except for the lack of a 'badger-face' its markings are just about perfect for present day breed standards (See p. 25 XIII).

During this same period, in neighbouring Jordan a beautiful mosaic floor was being constructed in the Coptic Church at Madaba, near modern-day Amman; it shows various animals, amongst which is a dark brown sheep with three large white patches on one side, two lateral horns and small ears (See p. 25 XIV).

It is interesting to find that there were spotted sheep in Italy at this date. Virgil, the son of a yeoman farmer, writing The Georgics between 31 and 30 B.C., maintained that if a white fleece was required for spinning then:

> 'the ram, however white he gleam,
> Have but a black tongue in his slavery mouth,
> Reject him lest he breed black-spotted lambs,
> And seek another in your teeming field.'

So far these scraps of evidence have been collected from around the Mediterranean and Arabia, but there is a far wider field to be covered.

Paintings of a famous episode in Chinese History have helped to confirm the existence of spotted sheep in the Northern Sung dynasty of 186-580 A.D., when the Empire was threatened by the Mongols.

The story goes that in 100 B.C. General Su Wu of the Han dynasty went on a peace mission to the threatening northern nomadic tribe of Hsiung Nu (the Huns); having been captured and tortured by them, he refused to enter their service. He was exiled to the north-west, together with a flock of rams with orders not to return until they had lambs. After several years the Han General, Li Ling was sent to persuade him to throw in his lot with his captors, as Li himself had done following his defeat in 99 B.C. Su's refusal made him a heroic exemplar of loyalty, to be admired by succeeding generations whenever a Chinese dynasty was threatened by barbarians from the north. This episode is the subject of 'The Parting of Su Wu and Li Ling' depicted in a number of paintings by various artists. One, a handscroll in Taiwan dating from the end of the Northern Sung dynasty shows Su's flock of sheep as very obviously spotted. (The artist seems to have preferred the idea of an all female flock, but perhaps this comes under 'artistic licence'.) Of interest to the modern flock master is the fact that these sheep are polled, two and four-horned, all tails are short, some up, some down, with one definite set of lop ears, whilst the rest of the flock have small ears. (See pp. 26 XVI) Most of these paintings are no longer extant but one, now in Stockholm, shows three sheep standing beside the Generals. These are spotted and two-horned and one has small lop ears. (See p. 13).

When a painting of merit changed hands in China it was usual for the new owner to apply his seal to the picture. One of the seals on the Taiwan painting belonged to the famous artist Chao Meng-fu (1254-1322). Two 17th Century catalogues refer to a painting by him entitled 'The Weeping Farewell of Su and Li' which now no longer exists.

III. Chinese 14th Century

His painting, known in Chinese as 'Painting of the Two Yang', is here reproduced as it would have appeared in its original form; the addition of some 24 seals and colophons by owners and admirers which are now to be seen on the picture very much detract from the beauty of the original See p. 26 XV).

The Chinese word 'yang' covers both sheep and goat, often used in contrast as 'shan mountain yang' usually meaning a goat, and 'mien soft yang' generally meaning a sheep. That these are portraits of the two animals is explained by the artist in his written note:-

> *'I have painted horses but not tried sheep [or goats]. Since Chung-Hsin asked me for a painting, I have playfully painted these from life. Although the painting cannot approach those of the ancient masters, it seems to have somewhat captured their spirit consonance.*
>
> *Tzu-ang [Chao Meng-fu]'*

Translated by Professor Chu-Tsing Li, the words 'spirit consonance' infers that the animals are 'alive'.

This portrait of a two-horned, small eared spotted sheep in full wool could be an artist's impression of a present day untrimmed show sheep.

The photograph reproduced on page 27, XVII of a wall hanging painted in pen and wash was probably a 16th Century copy of a far older Chinese painting. It shows a child in Mongolian-style clothes, riding a large white goat, with two lop-eared spotted sheep running beside. The child is carrying a sprig of plum blossom, a traditional New Year symbol. This composition may be a play on words, as the old word for sheep being a homophone (applied to words having the same sound but different meanings) also being Good Luck. This painting can therefore be called 'Welcoming Spring' or just 'Child with Three Sheep'.

The harness on the goat is identical to that worn by horses of the Yuan dynasty of 1280-1368 A.D.

Spotted sheep are documented in China from c.1000 A.D. until the present day. In the 17th and 18th Centuries beautiful works of art were exported from China to the European markets, often near repeats of each other. In 1978 and 1988 two almost identical mirror paintings were auctioned in London. The first in a contemporary Cantonese carved giltwood frame dating from the mid-18th Century, (A detail of which is shown here) the second in a large George III moulded giltwood

*IV. Cantonese
mid 18th Century*

overmantel divided by shaped mirror slips (See p. 25 XII). The pastoral scene shown in both, is of an elegantly dressed lady seated on a rock surrounded by her animals, her herdsman in attendance. In each picture there are six sheep/goats, three of which are definitely two horned, black and white sheep with downward falling tails, the position of the animals having been altered in the two pictures.

A Veterinary Surgeon, William Youatt (1776-1847), an original member of the Royal Agricultural Society, published his 'Sheep, Their Breeds, Management and Diseases' in 1837. He quotes from Navarett's Account of China:-

> '. . . . to the south. . . . a smaller, lower sheep of a more European character, and producing a fine and very useful long wool. The Chinese manufacture some good serges from it, not so close as those

made in Europe, but thinner and finer, and having a peculiar silky appearance. They likewise prepare a considerable quantity of felts of various colours. The largeness and beauty of the Chinese carpets have often been praised. An old traveller says that "when the Dutch [c.1784] presented the Emperor of China [probably Ch'ien Lung 1736-96] with some scarlet and other cloths made in Europe, he asked how, and what they are made of, being told, he replied that his subjects could make them, and therefore there was no need to bring them so far'.

V. Mongolian 1963 A.D.

The modern day photograph taken c.1963 shows a typical Jacob with the rather discouraging caption, 'Mongolian Ewe. Primitive type, probably cross bred'. Though in poor condition, this two horned ewe and the four-horned sheep in the background obviously carry much the same blood lines as today's badger faced, small eared Jacob sheep. The author quotes from Wagner (1926):-

> *'that China proper does not possess a native type of sheep evolved from the indigenous wild stock. All Chinese sheep are derived either from Mongolia or Tibet.'*

There remains the possibility that the Chinese (or Mongolian) spotted sheep were the ancestors of the biblical flocks noted in the Bible and earlier in this Chapter. It is an accepted fact that most cultures have moved from East to the West.

In India, the Mogul Emperor Jahangir (1569-1627) the son of Akbar The Great was interested in rare birds and uncommon animals and is likely to have commissioned the painter Basawan to paint the unsigned picture (See p. 28 XIX) of his tethered ram. This great artist was known for painting 'believeably tactile forms and to instill life into his subjects', so once again we have a portrait. This highly prized ram, duly adorned with a neckpiece of bells, has obviously been trimmed. Perhaps rather white for present day breed standards, he carries two horns, is badger faced, has small ears and is short tailed. It is interesting that the chain holding the ram runs to the equivalent of a modern-day bull tether.

The Mogul Emperor Babar known as 'Tiger' (1483-1530), founder of the Mohammedan Empire in India, may be the subject of the early 17th Century miniature (See p. 27 XVIII). He is holding a two horned, lop eared, stylized spotted ram with short downward tail, but without the badger face.

Of almost the same date is an unsigned pen and wash drawing of a magnificent four horned recumbent ram owned by the 8th Earl of Mansfield. The painting is from a set of four companion paintings which depict an eagle, a wild or hunting dog, and a snake, these presumably all being part of some Indian nobleman's menagerie. The ram is lop eared with a white face, perfectly balanced horns, and the markings very similar to those of the Assyrian ram (See p. 28 XX).

Spotted sheep were also being used in Europe during the 17th and 18th Centuries to represent 'pastoral scenes'.

This anonymous German drawing, dating from c.1650-1700 shows a polled Jacob with small ears together with a white sheep and a bearded goat.

A few years later at the Meissen porcelain factory (on the Elbe near Dresden) a polled, pied lamb with small ears and short tail was manufactured, probably by Kandler, a sculptor who superintended the modelling in hard porcelain from 1731. (See p. 100 LII)

VII. Italian/English, unknown date

The 8th Earl Fitzwilliam owned an 18th Century oil painting of three rather different looking sheep posed in front of the Spoleto Viaduct in Italy. This unsigned oil painting hung at Wentworth Woodhouse and has been attributed to George Stubbs. It shows a shorn, brown spotted, badger faced ewe with long tail, lop ears and brown legs. To the left there is an artist's impression of a Barbary sheep, between the two is an unclassified lop eared sheep. (See above)

In 1978, Lord Fitzwilliam wrote to the author:-

'I am at last sending you the photograph of the so-called Stubbs picture at Wentworth described in the Catalogue as of Jacob's Flock.

As you will see, only one of them bears any resemblance to what we think of as Jacob's and even that one has lop ears, which I do not think is right for Jacob's Flock, certainly by present day standards.

I hope this is of some use to you, please keep the photograph.'

VIII Italian
1723-1783 A.D.

In Italy Francesco Londonio (1723-1783) painted a shepherd boy resting by his two sheep with a bearded black and white goat. One sheep is white, the other badger faced with prick ears. (See above)

In 1837 Youatt (*Ib*) reproduced a wood-engraving signed 'J. Jackson'; the caption which he puts in brackets, reads 'Cyprus, or four-horned Sheep'. It is an excellent example of today's Jacob, with perhaps rather larger eyes. Youatt quotes from Mariti's Travels in Cyprus (Vol. I pp 35 and 225) as follows:

IX. Cypriot

> '*Many of these sheep are policerate (having more than two horns). They all spring from the frontal bones, the crest of which is elevated in a peculiar manner, in order to form their base. The central horns are usually straight, or somewhat divaricating — occasionally they are spiral; the lateral ones assume almost every possible variety of curve. The following cut represents the most frequent appearance of the Cyprus four-horned sheep.*'

Great store has been set by historians upon the number of horns which are carried by the various native, feral breeds of sheep found in Britain. Writing in 1913 Henry J. Elwes F.R.S. covers this point in detail in the 'Guide to the Primitive Breeds of Sheep and their Crosses'. He maintains that 'after many years of careful selecting none but four-horned rams to breed from, there are always a large percentage of ram lambs with only two horns'. This also applies to a modern day two-horned flock in which the odd unexpected four-horned lamb will appear, destined as is so often pointed out in old letters, to become 'excellent mutton'.

Referring to the origins of sheep (Encyclopaedia Britannica: Richard Lydekker and James Richie) there seems to be a very wide choice:-

The many Horned Sheep

> *'The variations of external characters seen in the different breeds are very great. They are chiefly manifested in the form and number of the horns, which may be increased from the normal two to four or even eight, or may be altogether absent in the female alone or in both sexes; in the shape and length of the ears, which often hang pendant by the side of the head in the peculiar elevation or arching of the nasal bones in some eastern races; in the length of the tail, and the development of great masses of fat at each side of its root or in the tail itself; and in the colour and quality of the fleece.'*

Much along the same lines that there are today several distinctive types of goat, both long and short eared, so it would seem was once the case for varying types of sheep, their fleeces remaining spotted. This same 'ingenious opinion', according to Youatt, had occurred to Charles Livingstone (1821-1873, brother of David) when writing 'Livingstone on Sheep' p44:-

> *'. . . . most of the sheep I have seen in Italy, have pendant ears. From this circumstance I presume that they have been longer domesticated than those of Spain or the other parts of Europe; . . . . I consider pendant ears as proof of very ancient domesticity, because I believe all wild animals carry theirs erect; and most, if not all of them, have the power of moving them to the point from which the sound is derived. When they cease to be their own protectors, and rely upon man both for defence and support, the organs given them with a view to these objects are gradually impaired, and the debility which results from their inaction changes their very form.'*

Syrian Goat

This was certainly the case in ancient China as reproduced in Plate XVI (p. 26) where the flock, though all spotted, have different characteristics.

Today the Jacob has particularly small ears compared to other breeds, (the black and white Dutch Friesland has larger ears and is polled). If a true blood line is sought then all the lop eared, spotted sheep afore mentioned must be disregarded. Those with small ears illustrated in this book are in date order:-

Sicilian water pot c.600 B.C.
Assyrian glazed vase 1st Century B.C. and
Mosaic floor, Jordan.
Chinese paintings 10th-18th Centuries.
German drawing c.1680.
Indian painting of ram 1569-1627.
Italian Shepherd Boy 1723-1783.
Meissen figure of lamb c.1745-50.
Yorkshire, figure of a ewe and lamb c.1810.
Cypriot sheep, pre 1837.
Chinese photograph 1963.

Another feature of these pied sheep, as seen from the illustrations, is that they were thin tailed, unlike the accepted idea of the times that most foreign breeds were fat-tailed. Except for the shorn Assyrian ram (and the 'Stubbs' ewe) it would appear from the detailed portraits that for practical purposes their tails had been cut short. In Elizabethan England when the ballad 'Little Bo-peep' was written, the fourth verse reads:-

Tartarian Sheep

> *'There she espied their tails side by side,*
> *All hung on a tree to dry.'*

These may have been bitten off by the shepherd as was common practice until early this century. Apparently they were considered a delicacy, as Mrs. Beeton in her 1906 'Household Management', had included two recipes for 'Lambs' Tails', one of which was from Russia. She notes:- 'Average cost: uncertain, lambs' tails being seldom sold. Seasonable from April to October'. This surely is evidence that lambing, as in modern day Jacob and Dorset Horn flocks, could take place three times in two years.

At the 1971 Royal Smithfield Show in London where Jacob sheep were shown for the first time, an old shepherd remarked, 'Oh I see you are showing God's sheep'. The centuries old Bible story, handed down from generation to generation was still very much alive. It is curious to find that it was not until the 18th Century that some flocks in the British Isles were called Jacob; other flocks consisting of the same pied sheep were called Syrian, Palestinian, Barbary, Algerian, Portuguese, Spanish and Persian, together with Piebald.

Geoffrey Chaucer may have been alluding to these sheep when he wrote the Pardoner's Tale, one of his Canterbury Tales in 1387. It is the story of a thoroughly disreputable 'priest' whose means of livelihood was to dupe the unsuspecting for a fee.

> *'Then in a metal box I have a shoulder bone*
> *Which came from a holy Jew's sheep.*
> *'Good men', I say, 'take notice of my words:*
> *If this bone is washed in any well,*
> *If cow, or calf, or sheep, or ox swell up,*
> *From eating a snake, or being stung by a snake,*
> *Take water from that well and wash its tongue,*
> *And it will be cured at once. And furthermore,*
> *Of pox and scabs and every sore*
> *Shall every sheep be healed that of this well*
> *Drinks a draught. Take heed of what I say:*
> *If the honest man who owns the beasts*
> *Will every week, before the cock crows,*
> *Before breakfast, drink a draught from this well,*
> *As that holy Jew taught our ancestors,*
> *His beasts and his stock shall multiply.'*

An editorial footnote referring to the first two lines of the passage explains that 'The shoulder bone of a sheep was often used in the Middle Ages in divining the future. The Pardoner's relic here would seem especially powerful since it had been associated with "an holy Jew", i.e. some Old Testament hero, possibly Jacob'.

Pure speculation, but surely if the itinerant wandering 'Priest' were to be leading a 'ringstraked and spotted sheep' this would prove beyond doubt to the illiterate peasant that he had been to the Holy Land in order to bring back this sacred relic.

Around Stratford-upon-Avon early in the 20th Century these sheep were still sometimes known as 'Shakespeare's Sheep'. The reason would have been that there is a strong local story that Shakespeare was caught poaching deer from nearby Charlecote Park where spotted sheep are said to have grazed in those early days.

What is certain is that Shakespeare referred to Jacob's flock in 1600 when he wrote 'The Merchant of Venice' in order to advise how one's possessions could be multiplied. In Act I Scene 3, Bassanio introduces his friend, a merchant of Venice, to Shylock, a rich Jew, in hopes of securing a loan of 3,000 ducats. An argument takes place concerning the interest payable.

'SHYLOCK *When Jacob graz'd his uncle Laban's sheep,*
This Jacob from our holy Abram was
(As his wise mother wrought in his behalf)
The third possessor; ay, he was the third,

ANTONIO *And what of him? did he take interest?*

SHYLOCK *No, not take interest, not, as you would say,*
Directly interest: mark what Jacob did.
When Laban and himself were compromis'd
That all the eanlings [new born lambs],
Which were streak'd and pied
Should fall as Jacob's hire, the ewes being rank
In end of autumn turned to the rams,
And when the work of generation was
Between these woolly breeders in the act,
The skilful shepherd pill'd [peeled] me certain wands,
And in the doing of the deed of kind
He stuck them up before the fulsome ewes,
Who, then conceiving, did in eaning [lambing] time
Fall parti-colour'd lambs, and those were Jacob's.
This was a way to thrive, and he was blest:
And thrift is blessing if men steal it not.'

The evidence so far discovered proves that pied sheep are of a very ancient lineage. It must always have been common knowledge that it is difficult to retain the breed's unique markings. Both Laban and Jacob's flocks had black sheep and to this day if Jacobs are crossed with any other pure breed (except Dorset Horn with which there is a breed-affinity) the offspring will be black, usually with a white spot on the head and tip of the tail. This fact of a dominant black gene is seen in the Egyptian illustration, Plate II where a black sheep has been included.

It is therefore important to study the facts confirming their existence in the British Isles. The majority of the many, now flourishing, flocks of Jacob sheep in Britain, Europe, America and Canada, owe their existence to the owners of parklands who took great trouble in the 17th and 18th Centuries to try to keep their flocks pure, two or four horns usually being of prime importance. These few inspired people collected rare animals, flowers and birds for their menageries and, as is true today in the 'Children's Corner' of Zoological Collections, the Jacob with its distinct spotted fleece and often multiple horns is an obvious curiosity. Some flocks were kept with deer in parks, purely as ornamental sheep to be admired from afar. It is from these often quite large flocks that our present day sheep are descended. Care was taken in those early days to obtain new blood, normally by an exchange of rams, but eventually in most cases interest waned, and the stock lost condition through neglect. Very few were shorn as nothing could be done with the coarse fleeces and some of the small lean carcasses were not worth using. By the end of the First World War many flocks had disappeared.

Those flocks that survived did so through the efforts of their proud owners who took the trouble to get stock from distant places, from Cheshire to Derbyshire, Buckinghamshire to Northamptonshire, Wales to Scotland and from Ireland to England. These flocks had been the lucky ones which had had the odd bale of hay tossed over the high deer fencing in a rough winter, or had accompanied the newly married daughter of the house to pastures new; thereby giving the modern breeder the choice of so many blood lines and the stamina which has come through to the present day.

When studying estate records and private papers it is important to bear in mind the various names used to describe these sheep. Great care has to be taken with the word 'Spanish' — sometimes it is used to describe the Merino, occasionally in connection with the 'Armada Legend' (see TABLEY); if the value or colour of the sheep is mentioned the difference is obvious.

James Farey (Senior) made a survey of Derbyshire in 1807 when he listed many different breeds of sheep. He writes:-

> 'the very large importations of Spanish Sheep which followed the advance of our Armies into the interior of that Country [led to the] greater facility of procuring Merinos. . . . in March 1813 'not less than 450 pure Merino sheep and 1,750 Merino-crossed sheep were kept in this County.'

Of great interest is the 10th type of sheep he mentions:-

> '10. Spanish, spotted coarse-woolled Sheep: these are of a dark brown colour spotted with white, with thick white tails, and they a good deal resemble some that I have seen among the fancy stock in Gentlemen's Parks, and were called Cape Sheep.'

(This refers to a very long argument, the details of which may be found in A. R. Werner's book 'An Enquiry into the Origin of Piebald or "Jacob" Sheep' published some ten years ago. Here evidence is given for and against spotted sheep having been imported into Britain from South Africa at the end of the 19th Century.)

Vita Sackville West, writing her Country Notes in 1939, included a charming article 'Jacob's Sheep', an extract from which reads:-

> 'King George III obtained Merino sheep from Spain some having been given him by the Marquesa del Campo de Alange. Merinos do not thrive in our climate, even under Royal patronage: Edward IV, who imported three thousand from Spain had already failed to make a success of them. Jacob sheep, on the other hand, thrive and multiply; the ewes habitually give birth to twins and even triplets; their enormous fleeces safeguard them from cold and damp; they are said to be hardier than our native breeds. The old gentleman who has charge of my small flock here [Sissinghurst Castle, Kent] has a pleasing theory about them: he is persuaded that they come from a mountainous country and that they stand for preference on the emmet-heaps [ant hills] as the nearest thing they can find to a mountain in Kent.'

Care should be taken with the word 'Barbary', used in estate papers and letters which also denoted pied sheep.

Writing of Morocco Sheep, William Youatt quotes from Major Hamilton Smith's 'Animal Kingdom' Vol. IV p. 326 who says 'Pedro IV of Spain [Peter IV 1356-1387 King of Aragon].... imported several Barbary rams for the improvement of the Spanish sheep; and two hundred years subsequently, the Cardinal Ximenes had recourse to the African rams for the same purpose.'

James Anderson LL.D. (1739-1808) in his 'Essays relating to Agriculture & Rural Affairs' Vol. II p. 245 writes:-

'in the province of Andalusia in Spain there is a race of sheep that are brindled and spotted black and white'.

In 1909, the author of 'An Effort to Trace the History of the so-called "Spanish" Piebald sheep.' Mr. Heatley Noble, (see TEMPLE COMBE) received a letter from Mr. Walter Fenwick stating 'That I saw piebald sheep at Ronda I am absolutely certain'. Both Andalusia and Ronda being in southern Spain, these two references substantiate why these pied sheep were called 'Spanish' by some flock owners.

Writing to the author in 1975, the late Mr. C. F. Colt noted:-

'I have just got back from Portugal where I noticed quite a number of Jacob's Sheep — or anyhow those that look very much like them .... Even quite near our house I noticed some spotted lambs. Normally the sheep seem to have quite large horns, black legs and a black nose, and the lambs seem to have a large circle of black round their eyes.'

Many flocks brought to the British Isles from Spain carried Barbary blood, and this explains why some flocks in British parks were so named.

BARBARY BREED OF WILD SHEEP
Cuvier

X. Barbary end of 18th Century

The true Barbary can be seen in this print entitled 'Barbary Breed of Wild Sheep' which shows the distinctive brown 'collar', white body and fat tail of this sheep. It is described in the 1929 Encyclopaedia Britannica as 'the only wild sheep found in Africa, where it inhabits all the mountain ranges of the north descending eastward far into the Sudan'. The mounted head of a Barbary sheep, shot by the author's father in 1912 when on Inspection in Kordofan, has the words, 'G. Haraza' which refers to the genus from Jebel Haraza in the Eastern Province of the Sudan. (See p. 100 L)

*XI. Skull of a species of sheep
formally kept at Gisburn Park (undated)*

XII Cantonese mid 18th Century

XIII Assyrian c.50 B.C.

XIV Judean c.50 B.C.

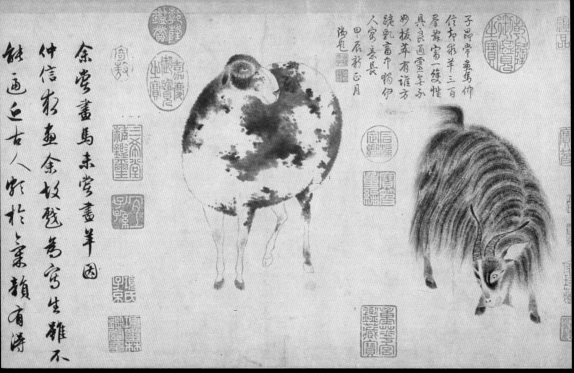

余嘗畫馬未嘗畫羊因
仲信求畫余故戲為寫生雖不
能逼近古人頗於氣韻有得

子昂嘗畫馬仲
信求余羊三百
羣嘗寫一雙惟
具良面靈至予
妙援萃有誰方
涘乳當中絢伊
人富玄長
甲辰新正月
溥儀

XV Chinese 1254-1322 A.D.

XVI Chinese, Five dynasties 906-960 A.D.

XVII Mongolian 16th Century

XVIII Indian early 17th Century

XIX Mogul 1569-1627 A.D.

XX Indian mid 18th Century

The Park Sheep Society

In 1911, some sixty years before the idea of forming a Jacob Sheep Society had materialised, Mr. H. J. Elwes and Professor Ewart had much the same idea. Their circular covered the seven types of Park Sheep whose pedigrees were likely to be lost. They also wished to eradicate the cross breeding which had been going on amongst some flocks as an 'improvement' or for experimental purposes.

Excerpts from their beautiful copper plate printed two-page letter are as follows:-

'It has been a common practice among many landowners to keep in their parks various breeds of sheep which are not generally known to those who keep sheep for profit only. Some of these little flocks are of very old standing and have been more or less carefully attended to by their Owners., ... valued as much for their ornamental qualities as for the wool and mutton they produce. . . . a most important [feature] is their ability to live like deer, on grass alone without the daily attention of a shepherd.

. . . . the sheep we desire to improve have no standard or pedigree, they are liable to degenerate by careless crossing, and as they are never seen at agricultural Shows, it is difficult to know where to find rams of good type.

The Royal Agricultural Society will only admit and give prizes to animals recognized as pure breeds, and until a Society for the improvement of Park Sheep is formed, such breeds as those we advocate must remain in their existing neglected condition.

Whether or not such a Society is formed and whether it can include in its scope distinct breeds is a question which cannot be answered until we know how many persons owning these breeds are inclined to join it. In order to ascertain this we request all those who take an interest in the subject to reply to the following questions:-

1. *What breed of Park Sheep do you keep?*
4. *Would you join a Park Sheep Society supposing that a Flock Book is started or otherwise?*
6. *Do you consider that any trimming or shortening of the tail is desirable, and have you noticed that long tails are decidedly useful to the sheep. . . .?*
(Note: This is proof that they were long-tailed; it has taken until 1988 for this rule, against too short tails, to come into force.)

Seven 'Park Sheep' are then listed, No. 6 reads:-

The pied sheep of Spanish or North African origin (sometimes called Syrian or Zulu sheep) the rams often with four horns.

Signed: J. J. Elwes,
Colesborne Park,
Nr. Cheltenham.

J. Cossar Ewart,
Pemnicuick, N.B.

Two years later in 1913 two small books were published, one by Mr. Heatley Noble of Temple Combe, Henley-on-Thames, Oxfordshire, the other by Henry John Elwes, F.R.S. of Colesborne Park, Nr. Cheltenham, Gloucestershire. Both these gentlemen had pied sheep. Many extracts from Mr. Noble's article are quoted in this book.

In Mr. Elwes' book 'Guide to the Primitive Breeds of Sheep and their Crosses. . . . With notes on the management of Park Sheep in England' he includes illustrations of pied sheep; as evidence, a footnote on page 9 reads 'My best five-year-old spotted ram has just had his horn broken off close to the head in fighting, March 16th 1913'.

He makes the point that the sheep kept in large parks are 'only occasionally visited by the shepherd and, in addition to their other good qualities, these sheep have an individual beauty and interest which makes them very attractive in parks and to persons who do not keep a large flock of sheep or a professional shepherd'. He then quotes from an article he wrote for the 'Year Book of the Amateur Menagerie Club 1913' of which extracts are here given:-

> '. . . . they will thrive better if thinly stocked on land which is grazed by deer, cattle, or ponies as well. I have noticed in my own park, that they usually prefer the higher and more exposed part of it. . . . When snow or severe frost comes they require some keep just as deer do . . . . A very marked feature in most of the mountain breeds is that the ewes are excellent mothers. It is rarely necessary to give the ewes any help in lambing, as the lambs get up and suck their own dams without any help, and however poor the ewes may be themselves, they usually have plenty of milk, so that the lambs grow fast as long as they are suckled. In large parks it seems doubtful whether it is better to wean the lambs or let them suck as long as they will. . . . But if they are weaned, both the ewes and the lambs must be kept in fences which they can neither climb, jump, nor get through, as until they settle down they are very difficult to keep in bounds.'

He goes on to say:-

> 'Personally, I am inclined to believe that they were all formerly two-horned, and that the second pair [of horns] may have been the result of a cross with some Northern breed such as Hebridean or St. Kilda.'

Note: Lord Mansfield, writing to the author in 1970 regarding his picture of a four-horned (See p. 28 XX) ram says:-

> 'This would rather knock Elwes's theory on the head and I must say that I do not subscribe to it. I do not believe that the breed originated in Shetland or the Hebrides.'

Mr. Elwes' book was re-published by the Rare Breeds Survival Trust in 1983; the then Honorary Director, now Past President Mr. Michael Rosenberg, C.B.E., made the following comment:-

> 'Of the 15 breeds of sheep now classified by the Trust as rare, four are discussed by Mr. Elwes in his book.

Belatedly, perhaps, we recognised the numbers of breeds that had become extinct and were heading for extinction, without any organisation making a concerted effort to reverse the trend. It was not until 1972 that a meeting of concerned farmers, scientists and advisers instigated the formation of such an organisation.'

The Rare Breeds Survival Trust became registered with the Charity Commissioners in 1973.

Meanwhile the embryo Jacob Sheep Society had been going from strength to strength. In July 1969 there were 78 potential members and 55 flocks totalling 1,681 Jacob sheep. Mr. Dudley Bowes of Watton Abattoir, who subsequently became member No. 71 of the Jacob Sheep Society, very kindly gave us £10 which was our first donation.

In the Summer of 1969 one sheet of hand typed paper was sent out to the few people known to the co-founders, Miss Hermione Bartholomew and the author. It was headed:-

Proposed formation of a
Jacob Sheep Society

Name:-

Address:-

Whether interested in joining a Jacob Sheep Society on the lines indicated in Lady Aldington's letter dated 31st July, 1969 and accompanying Minutes.

Please answer
"Yes" or "No"

Dated   1969

Reply required by 11th August 1969.

[*For details of how the J.S.S. came into being see:-*

'The First 10 Years of the
Jacob Sheep Society'

Available from the Secretary, Mrs. John Earll, The Pines, 242 Ringwood Road, St. Leonards, Ringwood, Hampshire BH24 2SB. Tel: Ferndown (0202) 894319. Price £4.00].

On 15th October 1969 the Jacob Sheep Society documents were signed and the first Committee formed. By the following month there were 96 members, over 2,700 sheep and the Society had been registered with the Charity Commissioners. The first Committee meeting was held in December.

Alas the response to the 1911 appeal to save our sheep is not known, however the result of the second appeal is to be found in the list of 'The First Hundred Members of the Jacob Sheep Society' on page 101.

During the past twenty years 3112 people or organisations have joined the Society of which 1220 are fully paid up Members. These are encouraged to register their sheep in order that the various blood lines can be identified, some of which can be traced back to the Park Sheep mentioned earlier. There are of course many unregistered sheep a proportion of which carry this same blood; it is therefore impossible to calculate how many Jacob sheep there are today, the only guide being the figures of lambs which have been registered since 1972 when the scheme started. These stand at 5,225 Ram Lambs and 34,775 Ewe Lambs, making a total of 40,000 lambs registered in seventeen years.

Some, like Mr. Elwes and Professor Ewart were worried that these sheep would be 'improved'. The following is an extract of an article by J. C. Greig and A. B. Copper entitled 'The "Wild" Sheep of Britain' which appeared in Oryx, the Journal of the Fauna Preservation Society,' December 1970:-

> '. . . . moves have been made (1969) to set up a Jacob Sheep Society . . . But if the Society succeeds with two of its three main objects, namely the improvement of the wool and the drawing-up of a breed standard for show exhibitors, there will inevitably be a loss of genetic material and the Jacob sheep will no longer be a primitive breed. Improving the wool must involve either the culling of unsatisfactory animals or the introduction of foreign genes for wool quality. It would be interesting to maintain some stock of unimproved Jacob sheep in parallel with the 'improved' stock, in order not only to maintain the widest range of genetic variability possible, but also, by using the control stock, to trace changes in the breed brought about by artificial selection.'

In the 15th June 1974 edition of The Ark, the monthly journal of the Rare Breeds Survival Trust, the 'Breed of the Month' was concerned with Jacob Sheep. The following is an extract:-

> 'The breed is the success story of recent years. Five years ago it was dismissed as an aesthetic feature of country parks and stately homes. In 1973 there were 342 registered breeders and approximately 5,000 registered sheep in the breed.
>
> Today there are two fairly distinct types of Jacob sheep, which can be designated 'Park' and 'Improved'. The former are those which have evolved in a purely ornamental role, while the latter have been developed as commercial sheep by progressive breeders. As might be expected there is a considerable difference between the performance of the two types as shown below.'

	Park	Improved
Mature body weight (ewe)	94 lb.	133 lb.
Lambing % born	189	207
Lambing % reared	179	189

The article ends with a nice accolade to our early members:-

> 'The progress of the Jacob in the last two or three years provides a blueprint for the conservation and development of other rare breeds. The basic ingredient is the enthusiasm of the breeders, to which must be added the identification of the qualities of the breed, a system for registration of breeding animals, and an effective promotion programme.'

Surely the portraits of the well fed pied sheep shown earlier in this book are evidence that we are nowadays getting back to the original animal; it was the neglected flocks which were so interbred, never shorn and expected to survive on scant pasture that gave the idea that they were small wiry sheep and classed as 'Wild'. Mr. John Thorley, Secretary of the National Sheep Association has always maintained that we are so lucky with our many blood lines to choose from. The original 'dormant genes', which carry such stamina, are being allowed to flourish by careful selective breeding programmes of our modern flockmasters.

The Society's First Officers
in 1969

President:	The Duchess of Devonshire
Chairman:	The Lady Aldington
Field Officer:	Miss Hermione Bartholomew
Secretary and Treasurer:	Mr. John Thorley for the N.S.A.
Solicitor:	Mr. Simon Smith
Hon. Auditor:	Mr. Peter Angell

The Hon. Lady Burrell
Mrs. Patricia Caudwell, J.P.
Miss K. M. A. Clark
Mr. Geoffrey Hyde
Mr. Frank Loftus
Mr. Geoffrey Purefoy

Presidents of the Jacob Sheep Society

1971-78	Her Grace The Duchess of Devonshire
1978-80	The Earl of Halifax
1980-84	Mr. Thomas Frame
1985	The Lady Aldington

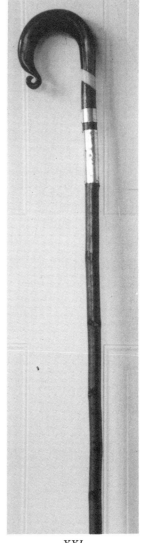

XXI.
PRESIDENT'S WAND
"IN MEMORY OF
CHARLES AVES"

Presented by this retired shepherd who had collected his small charge in order to pay for the Crook.

The late Mr. T. W. Lothian's sheep by St. Theobald's Church, Great Musgrave, Westmorland.

Flocks of Jacob Sheep in the British Isles

Pre 1969

An alphabetic list of the many parklands and farms which carried Jacob sheep, together with their owners names.

Unfortunately it has not been possible to identify a few names whom it is known had these sheep; equally some owners may have unintentionally been omitted. If any information is forthcoming it would be most welcome, in order that a fuller picture may be made in the future. See 'Information Required Please' p. 94.

Four lists have been used and co-ordinated where possible:-

1913: Compiled from the information collected by Mr. Heatley Noble, Temple Combe, Henley-on-Thames, Oxfordshire.

1953: The Old House, Withnell Fold, Chorley, Lancashire.

1964: Dr. Philip Ryder-Davies, 119 Stowey Road, Yatton, Somerset.

The fourth is an undated list compiled by Mr. Stephen Hobden (J.S.S. No. 879) from letters and information collected by word of mouth from various people. Letters from Colonel Henry Platt C.B. to and from Mr. Heatley Noble, destined for the dustbin, were saved by Professor R. T. White of Bangor University; as they concerned sheep, he gave them to Mr. Gwynne Williams B.Sc. head of the Department of Agriculture at The University, who in turn passed them on to Mrs. Lloyd Jones (J.S.S. No. 691). These were kindly lent to Mr. Hobden and the author.

Note: 'Listed' =

1913: Refers to the year Mr. Heatley Noble published his work:-
'An Effort to Trace the History of the So-Called
"SPANISH" PIEBALD SHEEP'
in which he notes all the information he has been able to collect regarding pied sheep in the British Isles; the page numbers are given as reference.

1953: Refers to a list of owners sent in that year to Lord Cranbrooke.

1964: Refers to a list of breeders of Jacob sheep sent to the author by Dr. Philip Ryder-Davies.

SH   Valuable information has been gathered by Mr. Stephen Hobden from early correspondence between owners of pied sheep and modern research.

An extract from one of Mr. Noble's letters written to Colonel Platt in 1910 show the frustration he suffered.

August 8th   'After weeks of trouble, and dozens of letters, I am no nearer the truth then I was when I started ! It seems almost impossible to trace the origin of the breed. It is all mixed up with legends, lies, and absurdities, but I have not given up hope and trust that my letters to Syria may bring forth fruit. In any case it is a most interesting subject, and I shall thank you for having started me on the hunt !'

Platt will have suggested that Noble try to find the origins of the Pied Sheep; eventually this research, mentioning so many Houses and Owners has made it possible to compile the '1913 List' as this was the year his book was published privately. On page 9 he notes 'I have particulars of about forty-one different flocks and doubtless there are many more unknown to me. . . .'

Here he was correct, to date 195 flocks have been discovered to have been in existence before the Jacob Sheep Society was formed in 1969. As will be seen later, of these 26 were listed amongst the first 100 Members of the Society — though several will have joined later; others will have had flocks of Jacobs which have never been listed.

When a source is known from letters, initials have been used as follows:-

Colonel H. Platt = P   Mr. Heatley Noble = HN

Capital letters for Properties have been used in the text to indicate where further information may be found.

It is hoped that the owner, at the date concerned, is given correctly, if this is not the case the right information would be most welcome.

ABERCAIRNY
Crieff, Perthshire

Colonel Home
Drummond-Moray b.1852

Origin of flock unknown, but in 1911 believed to have been at Abercairny at least 150 years, i.e. c.1760.

1817 'Farm Manager went to meet some Barbary sheep at Dundee. Where they came from I know not.'

(Letter dated March 1911 quoted by HN p. 10.)

1913 Listed: Crossed with other breeds. HN p. 10.

c.1898 Rams provided from WENTWORTH WOODHOUSE
-1909 (Fitzwilliam).

1932 Exchanged rams with TABLEY HN p. 10.

1964 The Abercairny Estates Ltd.

1989 J.S.S. No. 207.

AISLABIE PARK
Yorkshire

See: STUDLEY ROYAL
Ripon, North Yorkshire

c.1799 'There has been a breed of mottled sheep (brought originally from
-1802 Spain) kept at Aislabie park (I think) in Yorkshire for nearly half a century past, which still retain all their distinct peculiarities, if I be rightly informed, as pure as when first brought over. The wool of these sheep was in Spain of a very coarse quality, and of little value, as it is at this day in Britain. . .' From:- James Anderson Ll.D. 'Recreations in Agriculture, Natural-History, Arts & Miscellaneous Literature.'

1834 James Bell's 'Gazetteer' lists two locations in Yorkshire named Aislaby, one in the parish of Whitby, the second near Pickering.

Note: In August 1989 the publisher of this book, Mr. Robert Geering visited both these villages and was unable to find an Aislabie Park in either. It was suggested that perhaps the quotation might have been referring to 'Mr. Aislabie's park'. This would denote Studley Royal, near Ripon where Mr. John Aislabie had inherited the estate in 1699 from his mother, eldest daughter of Sir John Mallorie, Lord of the Manor of Studley. For connection with Yorkshire see W. M. Matthew's 'The Ill-Framed Knight' 1966.

At that time the Deer Park was already well established. During the late 18th and early 19th century the park was gradually made less formal in line with the fashion of the time and the influence of Lancelot (Capability) Brown and others.

ALDON
Yeovil, Somerset

Colonel H. C. C. Batten,
D.S.O., M.F.H. b.1883

c.1920 Ram from Warwickshire.

c.1925 Had original flock of 'Spanish' sheep.

1934 25th September flock consisted of:-

    1 Southdown Ram.
    1 Spanish Ram, 6 tooth.
    12 Spanish 2 tooth (1933).
    14 Spanish 4 tooth (1932).
    6 Black ditto (1932).
    12 Spanish 6 tooth (1931).
    19 Spanish full mouth.
Lambs 9 Chilver Spanish (1934).
    10 Black (to go to market).

1934 October. Sold to Miss Bouverie of DELAPRÉ ABBEY, Northampton:-

20 ewes at 70/- each:-
    6, 2 tooth (1933).
    6, 4 tooth (1932).
    8, 6 tooth (1931).

1936 December. Informed Auctioneers John Thornton, Hobson & Co. had 2 rams and 6 selected Chilver lambs for sale, all born Spring 1936.

Of interest is Colonel Batten's heading to his letter 'Spanish Spotted (or Jacob) Sheep'.

1938 April. Sold 6 Ewes and 9 Lambs to DUDLEY ZOO, Worcester.

1939 A large proportion of the flock sold to Mr. Burton of North Perrott, two of these ewes were to become the foundation stock of Colonel Batten's daughter, Mrs. F. E. D. Crook (J.S.S. No. 444).

1946 J. H. Batten of CHURCH FARM, Ryme Intrinseca, Nr. Sherborne, Dorset, son of above, had a small flock for a short time.

1964 Listed: See J.S.S. No. 444.

ALLERTON PARK
Knaresborough,
West Yorkshire

The Lord Mowbray and Stourton b.1867

1909 Flock owner. HN to P.

1910 'Impure flock of black sheep". HN to P

ANNESLEY PARK
Hucknall, Nottinghamshire

John Patricius Chaworth-Musters

1909 Owner of Piebald sheep. HN to P.

1913 '. . . . has flock of ten ewes. They came from Mr. Whitaker of RAINWORTH who obtained his stock from the late Sir Charles Tempest [BROUGHTON HALL] and parted with them in 1905'. HN p. 14.

Listed: SH.

THE ARGOED
Penallt, Monmouthshire

Major Y. R. M. Probert

1964 Listed.

ARLINGTON COURT
Barnstaple, Devon

Miss Rosalie Caroline Chichester b.1865

Mrs. Rosamund Winter of Arlington Rectory remembers two different flocks of Jacob Sheep at Arlington.

Pre 1926 The first small flock, acquired as a novelty by Miss Chichester sometime before 1926, were four-horned. These eventually died out.

c.1940 -43 The second flock, which arrived during the Second World War, also had four horns and were wild and unmanageable. It is thought they came from Dorset and travelled by train to the local junction to Arlington.

The fleeces were processed at Buckfastleigh and made into rugs, etc. for Miss Chichester's friends. The grand daughter of a maid from the house has a shawl, or rug, made from the Arlington Jacob sheep which she thinks dates from the 1930's.

When she became older, Miss Chichester would occasionally inspect her Jacob flock from her donkey cart.

A Mr. Peter Joyce from Shorlands Sheepskin Shop in Barnstaple remembers seeing sheep in the park sometime between the wars.

A Mr. Cox, who had handled fleeces from Arlington before 1948, had a letter from Miss Chichester around this date saying that she was trying to register her flock. However, her flock was not registered until much later.

During the Second World War, vests for seamen were knitted in Jacob wool by a lady who lived at Woolley Lodge, near to Arlington.

The property was eventually taken over by the National Trust.

The Chichester family owned land in Sussex, perhaps the sheep came from there.

(Information provided by Mrs. Shelagh Metcalfe, wife of the present National Trust Administrator of Arlington).

1964 Listed: A ram 'Harold' born on election day bought from author.

1969 J.S.S. No. 81.

1989 J.S.S. No. 81.

ASSINIBOINE PARK ZOO
Winnipeg, Manitoba, Canada

Director Clive G. Roots

1963 'The original group were imported from Whipsnade Zoological Park, Bedfordshire, England in 1963, and I believe they were the first to reach North America for many years.'
(Letter of 12.12.1978 to J. M. Ridley [HIGHGATES FARM] Ex J.S.S. No. 601 from the Director, mentions the sheep were known as Scotch Four-Horned Sheep.)

AVISFORD
Arundel, Sussex

Colonel A. J. Reynell Pack and Miss I. Pack

1881 See Dryden's letter to FitzGerald [SHALSTONE].

1881 Had sheep from Sir Henry Dryden [CANON'S ASHBY].

1909 'Miss Pack's sheep came originally from Canon's Ashby, Sir Henry Dryden, had a few beasts and I think was crossing them'. HN to P.

c.1909 Almost all sheep to Mrs. Farrer of INGLEBOROUGH. HN p. 12.

1910 'Miss I. Reynell Pack has given up'. HN to P.
Relationships:-
GARSCUBE, INGLEBOROUGH,
CUSWORTH, WESTON, Northamptonshire

BALLYWALTER PARK
Newtownards, Co. Down
Northern Ireland

The Lady Dunleath O.B.E.
b.1854

c.1900 2 ewes from Mrs. Smith Ryland of BARFORD to Lady Dunleath. HN p. 14.

1913 11 breeding ewes listed.
The present Lord Dunleath remembers 'they had always been known as Algerian Sheep, most had four horns, one with eight horns went to BELFAST ZOO. They had a reputation for freedom from foot troubles and were extremely good at getting free, fences meaning nothing to them, and once free were very difficult to round up.'

c.1958 30-35 sheep disposed of when the farm was being put on a sounder commercial footing.
Some years ago a ram and ewe were sold to Mr. McMillan of MIDDLE ROAD, Saintfield, Co. Down. J.S.S. No. 608.

BARFORD
Warwick

Mr. Graves and
C. I. P. Smith-Ryland

c.1860 The late Mr. Graves and Mr. Spencer Lucy [CHARLECOTE PARK] imported 2 rams from Spain. HN p. 13.

1891 15 breeding ewes from Gibbins of ETTINGTON. HN p. 13.

1910 Listed. HN to P.

1913 15 breeding ewes Listed.
Listed by SH.

BARNFIELD
Charing, Ashford, Kent

Mrs. V. Pym b.1896
Mr. M. H. Pym

c.1955 Foundation stock from SISSINGHURST.

1960 Gave Lady Aldington [THE KNOLL FARM] stock ewe lamb, foundation of flock. Supplied Miss Gladys Calthrop [LITTLE GAINS FARM] with a few ewes.

1964 Purchased Ram from Wales which was used for Knoll Farm ewe.

1964 Listed.

1969 J.S.S. No. 65. Mr. M. H. Pym (Southfield).

1989 J.S.S. No. 65.

BEELEY OLD HALL
Matlock, Derbyshire

Colonel C. R. Hodgson

1964 Listed.

BIDDLESDEN PARK
Nr. Brackley,
Buckinghamshire

George Manners Morgan
b. c.1821

c.1876 In 1989 Owen Jones of Blakesley maintained that his brother, who in 1876 was shepherd at BLAKESLEY HALL, fetched a four-horned ram, on loan 'of slightly different breed' from Biddlesden. As Mr. C. W. Bartholomew bought the Hall in 1876 it must have been after this date.

BILTON HALL
Bilton Ainsty, Nr. Wetherby,
West Yorkshire

Mr. Hall Plumer b. c.1755

Plate XLVI (p. 98)

1792 There was a flock of at least three Jacob sheep and two crossbred Jacobs.

This evidence has been taken from the oil painting which hung in the house until 1934 when it was sold by the then owner. Details of the provenance of this picture may be found in the Leger Galleries' Catalogue of their 1986 Exhibition.

As the artist Philip Reinagle R.A. (1749-1833) is known to have occasionally received co-operation from Sawrey Gilpin, R.A. (1733-1807) with the painting of animals, it is likely that he painted these sheep — as it is verified from Mr. Hall Plumer's Will that it was Sawrey Gilpin who had painted his horse.

A black and white print of this charming picture was reproduced in 1974 by A. R. Werner in his 'Enquiry into the Origins of Piebald or "Jacob" Sheep'. After exhaustive research, both in this country and America it transpired that it had been wrongly attributed to the artist James Ward, R.A.

Philip Reinagle, is known to have worked at Birdsall 'a neighbouring estate to BILTON for Lord Middleton'. Whose descendants lived at both WOLLATON and BOWDEN.

Possible Relationships:
　　TONG
　　TICHBORNE.

BLAKESLEY HALL
Nr. Towcester,
Northamptonshire

C. W. Bartholomew b.1854

Plate XXII facing

1880 Obtained sheep from Sir Henry Dryden [CANON'S ASHBY], which were photographed in the Chestnut Close at Blakesley Hall; the Tower, a mini folly, had an underground tunnel through to cellars of the Hall, thought to have been a gambling den.

Sheep always called 'Spanish'; Owen Jones, brother of the then shepherd, maintains (1989) that his brother fetched a four-horned ram, on loan, of 'slightly different breed' from BIDDLESDEN PARK.

1923 March 21st and 22nd. Auction at The Angel Hotel, Northampton Here 6 lots of 'A mounted Ram's Head' were sold from the 'Natural History Specimens' section. According to Miss Hermoine Bartholomew, grand-daughter of Charles William Bartholomew, these must have been Jacobs as no other breed were kept.

Plate XXIII facing

1931 Photograph of Miss Hermoine Bartholomew, co-founder of the Jacob Sheep Society, bottle feeding two 'Spanish' lambs at Blakesley Hall.

1947 September 23rd, an eight day sale took place; Lot No. 2523 'Four mounted Antelope heads and sundry antlers' sold for 10/-. 'These were the multi-horned ewes — as they came from the staircase to the Library, which is where they were hanging.'
(Hermoine Bartholomew 1989)

XXII. The Park c.1880

In the Livestock section it is interesting to see what had been kept during the 1939 wartime:-

Dairy Cattle

1. Red Poll Cow, due to calve October	£51
2. Red Heifer in milk	£29
3. Blue Roan Heifer due to calve October	£51
4. Red Poll Heifer Calf	£14

Horse

Black Mare, quiet and good worker	£18 7s. 6d.

Sheep

7 Spanish ewes @ £5 16s. 0d.	£40 12s. 0d.
13 Black lambs @ £5 9s. 0d.	£70 17s. 0d.

Note: These black lambs might have been the reason for collecting a four-horned Jacob from Biddlesden in order to get pure blood back.

Some of the above information has been supplied by Philip B. Kingstone, Dale Top, Blakesley.

1964   Listed as SAHAM, Thetford, Norfolk, Miss C. H. Bartholomew. Ex J.S.S. No. 3.

XXIII. See 1931

BOWDEN PARK **Chippenham, Wiltshire** *Sir Reginald Hardy, Bt.* *b.1848*	c.1883 14-15 ewes from CANON'S ASHBY. HN p. 12 1913 Listed: 14-15 ewes. *SEE DUNSTALL HALL.*

BRADDEN
Nr. Towcester,
Northamptonshire

J. M. Grant Ives

1904 Sir Alfred Dryden [CANON'S ASHBY] writing to Miss Reynell Pack [AVISFORD] from Colonel Platt's house Gruinards, Ross-shire:-

'. . . I will ask my Shepherd whether we can manage what you want in the way of spotted Sheep. Ours belong to my son but he lets me manage them. There are always some to dispose of at the proper times and it may be that an exchange for your Ram lamb would suit both of us, tho' I presume that J. M. Grant Ives' flock are descendants of the Ashby flock. Still he may have got a cross from some other flock.'

Listed SH.

BRAMHAM PARK
Wetherby, West Yorkshire

Colonel F. G. W. Lane Fox
b.1899

1964 Listed.

1969 J.S.S. No. 50.

1989 J.S.S. No. 245.
Relationship:- GARROWBY

BREACHACHA
Isle of Coll, Agyll, Scotland

C. K. M. Stewart

c.1967 Saw a flock of Jacobs in a field by Stirling Castle, asking the local farmer where he could get some, Miss Helen Hamilton [WHITEHOPE] was suggested where he bought 5 Ewes and a tup.

BROAD OAKS
Ludlow, Shropshire

Mrs. G. E. Burgess

1950 Two Jacob ewes brought, as a joke, by carrier from Shrewsbury
-60   Market, with some cattle. A Jacob ram could not be found, so they were put to a Dorset Horn.

1953 Put to a Jacob ram.
-63

1969 J.S.S. No. 64.

BRODSWORTH HALL
Doncaster, South Yorkshire

The Hon. Charles Thellusson
b.1868

c.1898 Rams provided from WENTWORTH WOODHOUSE.
-1909

1910 'Flock is sold'. HN to P
Relationship:- GARROWBY

BROUGHTON HALL
Skipton-in-Craven,
Yorkshire

Sir Charles Tempest b.1834

1905 Sold flock to Mr. Whitaker of RAINWORTH, and so on to ANNESLEY. HN p. 14.
Relationship:- BILTON, TICHBORNE, TONG.
A very successful breeder of Short-horn cattle — no reference to Jacob Sheep. (Present owner to author 1988).

BULSTRODE
Gerrard's Cross, Oxfordshire

The Duchess of Portland
b.1715

Plate XXIV facing
Two letters from Mrs. Delany to 'Mary' while staying at Bulstrode:-

1768 6th September.
'Went out again in the chaise after breakfast saw the two crown Birds & rams with horns standing thus the wool dark brown & white. Came home at half hour after four, work a little sauntering about the house looking over Prints finished the day & I left Her Grace last night better than she has yet been at half an hour past eleven which we have yet never exceeded.'

Czartoryske yet. went out again in ... Saw the two crown Birds & ram ...nding thus ... the wool dark brown & ...ne at half hour ... after four; took a little ...house & looking over Prints finished the

Guinea Fowl

1768 4th October.
'The Dss & I took a short walk in the morning and were driven home by the rain, a pretty and uncommon scene is now before me on the Lawn, a flock of sheep Shepherd & Dog at a little distance; & in the foreground (to talk like a painter) 15 or 16 Horses feeding with Peacocks & Guinea fowl that make a Beautifull mixture of pretty objects.'

'Mary' was Miss Dewes.

The Prints referred to are the beautiful paintings executed by Mrs. Delany, née Granville (1700-1788). Some of which are reproduced in Mrs. Ruth Haydon's book 'Mrs. Delany, her Life and her Flowers', a British Museum publication.

Relationship:- CHATSWORTH.

BURGHLEY HOUSE
Stamford, Lincolnshire

*Henry, 1st Marquess
of Exeter b.1754*

1797 Lancelot Brown (1716-1783), the landscape architect, known as 'Capability' Brown (because he was reputed to tell patrons that their estates had 'great capabilities') made notes of his visit to Burghley. He described the view as including 'herds of deer, droves of cattle and flocks of Spanish Sheep'.
(From 'A History of Burghley House of 1797' by J. & N. Eddowe p. 192).
Relationship:- MANVERS PIERREPONT

CALSTONE
Calne, Wiltshire

Mrs. P. Luard

c.1965 Had six Ewes from Mr. Gent [SUDDENE PARK FARM].

c.1966 These went to Mr. Wales [SCOTLAND LODGE], only 5 returned due to too active ram.
Later years used MILTON & SHALSTONE rams.

1969 J.S.S. No. 25.

1989 J.S.S. No. 25.

CALVERLEIGH COURT
Tiverton, Devon

Lady Heathcoat Amory

c.1980 Inherited J.S.S. No. 43 from THE OLD HOUSE, Sutton Courtenay.

CAMPSEA ASHE
Wickham Market, Suffolk

Hon. W. Lowther b.1855

1910 All black sheep. HN to P.

CANON'S ASHBY
Woodford Halse,
Northamptonshire

*Sir Henry Dryden, Bt. b1818
Sir Alfred E. Dryden, Bt.
b.1821
Sir Arthur Dryden, Bt. b.1852*

Several letters written by the two brothers, Henry and Alfred Dryden between 1881-1884 still exist; information from these letters follow.

c.1820 Mrs. Lush of THORPE MANDEVILLE (who had died before 1840) provided Colonel Hutchinson of WESTON, Weedon Leys, Northamptonshire with sheep, these in turn came to CANON'S ASHBY. This information does not tally with a letter of 1909 from Sir Alfred Dryden where he says:-

c.1845 'My brother was intimate with a Capt. & Mrs. Byrne of the Artillery when quartered at Weedon near here. Mrs. Byrne was a Spanish lady and told my brother of the breed; and she got her friends in Spain (what part of Spain I know not) to send my brother the half dozen or so of sheep which began my brother's flock. That will be about 64 years ago. She spoke of the breed being quite numerous then in Spain, and it is rather strange that they should have so entirely disappeared from that Country'.

In a letter of 1884, Sir Henry Dryden says that he had had the breed from 'a neighbour who had been in the Peninsular War'. [1808-14].

c.1824 Writing in 1884 Sir Henry said, 'I call the spotted sheep "Spanish". They have been for 60 years or more in this neighbourhood. I had the breed from a neighbour who had been in the Peninsular War and he called them Spanish; though I don't remember having asked him if he saw similar in Spain'.

c.1880 'Spotted sheep are common in the Basque Provinces and I have seen many in Shetland which has trade with Spain'. This point is enlarged upon in another letter as follows:-

'An officer told me that he has seen such in the Basque provinces and there are many in Shetland more or less spotted, and Shetland has great trade with Spain. The Shetland people don't like the *spotted* ones, so the marking is not distinct, not being desired; that is, the spotted ones are got rid of.'

'Mrs. . . . . oup (probably nee Miss L. Reynell Pack of AVISFORD) told me that her Grandfather, General Hely-Hutchinson was presented with some in 1841 when he was leaving Cape of Good Hope where he was Governor.

Copied by me in 1934 A.D.'
(Sir Alfred was then aged 82.)

Note 1: Colonel Henry Hely-Hutchinson of WESTON 1790-1874, married Harriet Wrightson of CUSWORTH, in 1825.

Note 2: Either Colonel Henry became a General, or it was Sir Walter Hely-Hutchinson who was Governor of the Cape 1901-1910.

In a 1909 letter from Sir Arthur he writes:-

'Many years ago a Spanish beggare woman came here carrying a child on her back. I told her I could not speak Spanish. "But" she said, "There are many of my countrymen here". I made out that it was the *sheep*, and she explained that when the child saw the sheep it cried out that it recognized countrymen. I asked her more and she said there were numbers of them where she lived, but I forget what part of Spain. The Merino sheep are totally distinct.' HN p. 1.

Writing in 1913, Mr. Heatley Noble mentions many transactions with stock from and to CANON'S ASHBY; These are listed together with details taken from correspondence with Colonel H. Platt.

1839 Writing in 1897 the late Sir Henry Dryden says, 'Mine came from -40 Colonel Hon. H. Hely- Hutchinson' [WESTON, Northamptonshire] about 1839 or 1840. He had them from THORPE MANDEVILLE, where the breed had been for many years, probably about 1800'. HN p. 11.

1840 Sir Henry believed that Mr. Vernon of STOKE PARK, Nr. Towcester, had these sheep. Also that Mr. Cartwright had them at EDGECOTE.

'In 18.. I changed rams with Lord de Tabley of TABLEY COURT near Knutsford.

In 18.. I changed rams with the Duke of Devonshire [CHATSWORTH].

In 18.. I sold 3 or 4 to Mrs. FitzGerald of SHALSTONE.

In 18.. Mr. Cartwright gave up the breed and I bought all he had.

Lord de Tabley's rams had usually 4 straight horns till he crossed with mine after which many had curled horns. Ours have almost always curled horns. The breed have been at Tabley for nearly 200 years as they are shown in a painting of the house of which the date is known.' (See TABLEY where this picture shows white sheep.)

c.1850   SHALSTONE supplied by Sir Henry with sheep, according to Admiral Purefoy. HN p. 12.

1879   Ram to TABLEY. HN p. 11.

1880   Exchanged rams with TABLEY. HN p. 11.
-1887

1881   Sir Henry supplied Miss Pack [AVISFORD] with sheep. HN to P.

c.1883   Sir R. Hardy [DUNSTALL] had 14-15 ewes from late Sir Henry.

Pre   Sir Henry provided sheep to Sir Robert Loder [LEONARDSLEA]
1887   which went on to Sir Merrik Burrel [FLOODGATES].

1904   Sir Alfred E. Dryden writing to Miss Reynell-Pack 'The spotted sheep belong to my son' offers to exchange a ram lamb.

1908   Listed by Richard Lydekker in his 'Guide to Domesticated Animals.' p. 21.

1909   Offers ram to Colonel Platt.

1913   Listed. Ram lamb from INGLEBOROUGH See Illustrations.

1920   There is a familiar modern-day ring to the following
-21   correspondence:-

August 12th '20, Mrs. Mulliner [CLIFTON COURT] to Sir Alfred:-

'I understand you keep black and white Spanish sheep so write to know if you have a young ram you could exchange with me for a shearling ram which I bought last year from Mrs. Noble, PARK PLACE, Henley-on-Thames. I am keeping on some of my lambs so want a change of blood.'

August 16th '20:-

'Many thanks for your reply to my enquiries for a Spanish ram. The one I want to change is a four horned ram, but he broke one coming here last autumn and another when he was being sheared lately. That first one that was broken is growing again — my this year's lambs by him have four horns — if you do not object to his having lost his horns I should like to exchange him for your ram with four horns.'

April 8th '21:-

'I was pleased to receive your letter today suggesting that we should exchange ram lambs. I will keep a good four-horned ram lamb for you and will be much obliged if you will keep one of yours for me.'

1934   Sir Arthur Dryden writing to Admiral Purefoy [SHALSTONE]:-

'I have more confidence in my late Uncle's written note than in my father's memory on an event happening when he was little more than a boy. Though they were rare half a century back [1884] there are now many flocks about the country.

Of interest are the descriptions of life at Canon's Ashby by Sir Alfred Dryden b.1821.

c.1836 'Until the railways came it [CANON'S ASHBY] was very inaccessible and the roads very bad. In my young days the roads were largely unfenced and when I drove to Banbury on my way to Winchester, through Oxford, on the first six miles of the drive there were 25 gates to be opened. It took two days to get there.'

1844 Sir Henry Dryden was Sheriff of the County in 1844 'and had escorted Queen Victoria on the 46 mile journey from Weedon to BURGHLEY HOUSE'.

The following notes were made in 1989 by his Great Grandson, Peter Wilfred Dryden, b.1921, which describe life at CANON'S ASHBY in 1938-40.

1911 'Arthur [b.1852] was fond of cycling, he often rode his bicycle the 70 miles from London to Ashby after his father's death. When the War ended in 1918, Bert Mood came home safe and sound to take charge of the horses. . . . Somewhere about 1923 or 1924 the horses were disposed of. . . . Bert was given half an hour's tuition on the maintenance of the car and how to drive it by the garage staff. . . . fortunately there was less traffic on the roads, and the greatest danger arose from horses becoming alarmed at these strange noisy vehicles they had never seen before. One of Bert's jobs was to mow the lawns. A pony was kept to draw the machine, and the pony wore leather shoes to prevent its feet damaging the turf. . . In the 1930's John Ward, an Eydon lad was employed to help in the garden, he and the ex-maids all say the food was good and plentiful, but rather monotonous, so many rabbits in the winter, and a lot of mutton, for the Spanish and Jacob sheep were killed and eaten in the house. Venison came to the table whenever deer were killed, the Drydens liked theirs hung to ripen, the maids ate theirs fresh. As far as possible the household lived on their own produce, cows were kept to provide milk and butter; the pigs killed for bacon and hams, then the kitchen garden provided an abundant supply of all sorts of fruits and vegetables. . . . As far as they possibly could, all the old customs were maintained on the estate during this period. The logs were exactly the same size and shape that they were in Sir Henry's day, only now a steam engine was hired to do the sawing. . . .'

'. . . . About 1935 Jim Tomlin had an accident when shooting deer in the park. He shot two instead of one, killing one and wounded the other, his sight was failing for he was getting on in life. He had been an expert at the job. . . . using the ancient muzzle loading gun. . . .'

The two photographs here illustrated are of particular interest; made into post-cards, presumably to send to other flockmasters, each are dated 1913 and the two groups of sheep stand in front of identical fencing.

On the back of the one of three lambs is a note:- See XXV

'The Ram lamb under the X was sent to Canon's Ashby on 18th Augt. 1913 by Mrs. Farrar [INGLEBOROUGH] in exchange for a Ewe lamb from the flock at Canon's Ashby but died before it could be used.' Initialled A.D. (Alfred Dryden.)

Across the card in Sir Henry Dryden's writing are the words:- 'Ingleborough Ram Lambs'.

These are four very nice four-horned lambs.

The second card (See XXVI facing) of three rams has 'Ingleborough Rams 1913' on the reverse in Sir Henry's writing. Each ram is identified in a hand written caption which reads:-

XXV.

Charlecote. *Lady* *bred from* [handwritten]

XXVI. Charlecote	Lady	Bred from
	Leicester Warren	Syrian
'Spanish'	'Persian'	'Syrian'

As we know from the CARSCUBE Estate Factor 'I understand Mrs. Farrar has used a Syrian Ram' it would seem that these three rams originated from CHARLECOTE, TABLEY and INGLEBOROUGH. As it is unlikely all seven sheep came from Ingleborough it would appear that we now know the origin of four of the sheep, leaving the three ram lambs as perhaps having been bred at Canon's Ashby.

Note: This proves conclusively that the CANON'S ASHBY and CHARLECOTE 'Spanish' sheep, the TABLEY 'Persian' sheep, and the INGLEBOROUGH 'Syrian' sheep were all one and the same breed, now known as Jacob Sheep.

Two small points may be of interest, one that the postage was 'A half-penny stamp for inland, one penny foreign' and that the Northamptonshire Record Office who hold these photographs are now in DELAPRE ABBEY.

Relationships:- HAZLEWOOD CASTLE, FLOODGATES

CANWELL HALL Sutton Coldfield, Warwickshire	1913	30 breeding ewes.
	1913	10 ewes presented by Mr. N. Gibbins of ETTINGTON; William Gibbins had got sheep from CHARLECOTE in 1881. HN to P. Listed SH.
P. S. Foster, M.P.		
[*Sir H. S. Foster, M.P.* *b.1855 Homelands,* *Henley-on-Thames.*]		
CARLTON FOREST **FARM** Worksop, Nottinghamshire	1964	When one year old went to a cattle sale where Mr. Frank Loftus (Ex J.S.S. Member 54) gave her two ewe lambs, and later a ram which had come from CHATSWORTH.
Miss Jane Baddiley	1969	J.S.S. No. 66.
	1989	J.S.S. No. 66.

CASTLE COMBE
Chippenham, Wiltshire

C. Lowndes b.1868

Sir John Eldon Gorst
M.P., K.C., b.1835

1855 Assumed name of Lowndes.

1887 Started flock with a Ram and a Ewe from late Countess of Cowley [DRAYCOT PARK] which had been imported from Zululand; these were crossbred, black sheep. They were crossed with Pied sheep from Mr. Whitaker and those of Mrs. Farrar [INGLEBOROUGH].

1892 2 rams from Prince Hatzfeldt [DRAYCOT PARK].

1892 1 ram from Mr. Whitaker. HN p. 15.

Writing in his Sheep Book, Mr. Lowndes describes the sheep as 'all black or nearly so, with only the face, tail and a leg or two white, and they never had more than two horns. . . . Mottled and four-horned sheep have subsequently been introduced into the CASTLE COMBE flock, and the two strains have now become thoroughly mixed'.

1908 Listed by Richard Lydekker in his 'Guide to Domesticated Animals.' p. 21.

1908 400 crossbred ewes and lambs.

c.1909 All sold with exception of 25 ewes.

1910 'Mr. Lowndes' flock went to Sir John Gorst with the Estate.' HN to P.

1913 Listed.

CATTON PARK
Norwich, Norfolk

Mr. George Morse

Pre 1840 Mr. Heatley Noble writing to the Rev. H. G. Morse had the following reply:-

'My father George Morse lived at Catton Park, near Norwich, where he had a small flock of black and white piebald sheep, perhaps a dozen or more, merely kept as ornamental animals. He died in 1852 when I was twelve years old and, as a young boy, naturally did not take much interest in the history of the sheep except that they were pretty and uncommon. When my father died the place was sold and doubtless the African sheep also. I always understood that the original pair had been given my father (who had been in the Army) by a brother officer who had got them in South Africa.' HN p. 4.

CHADDESDEN
Derby, Derbyshire

Sir Robert Wilmot, Bt.
b.1765

1811 Had 6 theaves and 3 lambs from Lord Middleton at WOLLATON in Nottinghamshire. Quoting from 'A General View of the Agriculture and Minerals of Derbyshire by James Farey (Senr.):-

'I have seen Spanish sheep in Gentlemen's Parks. . . . these are of a dark brown colour spotted with white, with thick white tails, and they a good deal resemble some, that I have seen among the fancy stock in Gentlemen's Parks, and were called Cape Sheep.'

CHARLECOTE PARK
Stratford-upon-Avon,
Warwickshire

Sir Thomas Lucy b. c.1609

1805 From Wellesburne Hasting — Warwickshire:-

'. . . . on the left two miles away is Chirlcote (sic) (John Lucy Esq.). Thomas Lucy, who built the house in the time of Elizabeth, is said to have driven Shakespeare from the county for stealing his deer.'

In a letter dated 1910 to Mr. Heatley Noble, Sir Fairfax Lucy (b.1870) writes:-

'They have been at Charlecote I believe for several generations. They have always been four-horned. . . . My brother [b.1876] was a pupil of the Agent at Charlecote, and told me that the late Mr. Spencer Lucy [Henry Spencer Lucy, b. c.1840] and the late

1860 Mr. Graves of Barford imported two rams from Spain in the sixties.' HN p. 13.

c.1881 30 breeding ewes to Mr. William Gibbins. These went on to CANWELL, ETTINGTON and BALLYWALTER.

1910 Sheep to Miss Vaughan of NANNAU or NEINAU Dalgelly, Wales. HN to P.

In Lady Alice Fairfax-Lucy's 'Charlecote and the Lucys':-

'There is a flock at Charlecote Park belonging to Sir Fairfax Lucy, the ancestors of which are said to have come from Portugal. The following is an extract from a letter by Sir Fairfax Lucy, November 10th, 1910. "I have looked up the sheep in a book of records we have, and all I can find about the sheep is this. A letter written by my grandfather, from Lisbon, Rue d'Estrell, on January 13th 1756, in which it is stated 'Mr. Geo. Lucy remained in Portugal till June and brought with him the ancestors of the flock of white spotted sheep that graze in the Park amongst the deer'".

The County Archivist (M. W. Farr) writes to the author in May 1989 as follows:-

'I am not clear about the letter dated from Lisbon on 13 January 1756. We know from the housekeeper's book (L6/1476) that George Lucy left for Lisbon on 24 October 1755 and returned to Charlecote in June 1756. However, a letter dated 13 January could hardly refer to the fact that "George Lucy remained in Portugal till June and brought with him the ancestors of the flock of white spotted sheep that graze in the Park amongst the deer". One presumes that the information which Sir Fairfax Lucy quoted in 1910 did exist but it does not seem to be amongst the Lucy papers we have.'

1913 36 breeding ewes.

1954 Listed.

Note: Until recently the older villagers called these sheep 'Shakespeare's Sheep' — see page 20.

1964 Listed.

1969 J.S.S. No. 5.

1989 J.S.S. No. 5.

CHATSWORTH
Bakewell, Derbyshire

The Duke of Devonshire
b.1720

1762 'To Mr. Eyre's Keeper for eight spotted lambs sent to his grace for £1 1s. 0d.' Probably Mr. Francis Eyre of nearby Hassop. (Account Book 1757-60 p. 61. re.176).

'6 mottled sheep from Mr. Clarke of Sutton Scarsdale for £3 2s. 0d.' Paid to John Bacon, probably a tenant. (folio 205v).

1804 '7 Spanish sheep sold to Thos. Bossley, a local man (folio 36).

1806 '5 Spanish sheep sold to Thos. Bossley.' (folio 117).

1809 '3 Spanish sheep sold to Thos. Bossley.' (folio 31).

'6 Spanish sheep sold to Thos. Bossley.' (folio 37).

(Details from Estate Account Books)

Note 1:

These sheep have always been known as 'Spanish' and it is possible that this originates from the fact that the wrecks of the galleons of the Spanish Armada were driven ashore on the west coast of Ireland. (See TABLEY). The 4th Duke of Devonshire was Lord Lieutenant of Ireland in 1755. He died in 1811. His daughter married in 1766, William, 3rd Duke of Portland [WELBECK ABBEY].

Note 2:

As mentioned before (see p. 22) Care should be taken when Spanish sheep are mentioned in old Estate Papers. In the Account Book of

Merino Ram

1809/10 18th September 1810 (opp. folio 67) is the following entry:-
'Paid Daniel Smith for 31 Spanish sheep bought at Colonel Downie's sale at Islington, six Rams and twenty-five Ewes for £646 5s. 6d.'

Jas. Mathison the Chatsworth bailiff was sent down to attend the sale and they were undoubtedly Merinos; the price paid was enormous. They were to be the foundation stock for a considerable flock which in 1817 produced 74½ stone of wool at 3s. 0d. a pound. (Farm Accounts for Nov. 1817 f.l.v.) See H. B. Carter's 'His Majesty's Spanish flock' Published 1964.

The author is indebted to Professor Peter Kup for all information from Chatsworth Farm Accounts and Note 2.

1819   Flock remembered by 7th Duke of Devonshire (b.1808) HN p. 9. Originally a two-horned flock.

1851   Rams from MILTON.

c.1879   Ram to TABLEY.
-1887

1881   Listed by Sir Henry Dryden [CANON'S ASHBY], who had sheep from Chatsworth.

1840   The 7th Duke of Devonshire (b.1808) exchanged rams with
-1881   Sir Henry Dryden [CANON'S ASHBY].

c.1881   Mr. J. Middleton Howells [HIGHFIELD] had sheep from Chatsworth. HN p. 9.

c.1906   Ram to WENTWORTH WOODHOUSE.
-07

1908   Ram to GORDDINOG son of above ram.

1908   Listed by Richard Lydekker in his 'Guide to Domesticated Animals.' p. 21.

The Lady Dorothy Macmillan (b. 1900) told the author that, as children at Chatsworth, they used to be made to wear very scratchy skirts made of Jacob tweed which her father (Duke of Devonshire born 1895) had had woven by students at Leeds University of which he was Chancellor from 1909. See SHANBALLY.

1913   24 breeding ewes; origin unknown; now four-horned, HN.

1953   Listed.

1958   Ram called 'Hartington' to MELBURY.
-64

1964   Listed.

1969   J.S.S. No. 20.

1971   Her Grace the Duchess of Devonshire was First President of the
-78   Jacob Sheep Society.

1989   J.S.S. No. 20.

Note: Bolton Priory, Skipton, North Yorkshire has had Jacobs from Chatsworth since at least 1980; those at Lismore Castle, Waterford, another of the Duke of Devonshire's Estates, brought new blood to the few flocks still existent in Ireland until c.1984.

Relationships:- WELBECK, BULSTRODE,
                LITTLE GLEMHAM.

CHIDEOCK MANOR **Nr. Bridport, Dorset** *Lt. Col. H. J. G. Weld, M.C.*	1958	Bought a ram and 3 ewes from a farm on top of a hill at Kingstone in a howling gale.
	1968	J.S.S. No. 23.
	1970	Sold 4 or 5 ewes to Lady Montagu of Beaulieu [THE PALACE HOUSE].
	1972	Sold flock. Relationship:- LULWORTH

CHURCH FARM **Ryme-Intrinseca,** **Nr. Sherborne, Dorset** *Mr. J. H. Batten*	1946	Had sheep from ALDON stock, via Mr. Burton of North Perrott. Relationship:- ALDON

THE CLIFF **Warwick, Warwickshire** *Sir Michael H. Lakin Bart.* *b.1846*		Flock came originally from his uncle Mr. Graves of BARFORD.
	1913	Has flock of 12-15 breeding ewes.
	1911	Told Mr. Heatley Noble of sheep at Madrid Agricultural Show. HN p. 16. Relationships:- HAMMERWOOD, KNEPP.

CLIFTON COURT **Rugby, Warwickshire** *Mrs. A. Mulliner*	1919	'Spanish' four-horned ram from Mrs. Noble [PARK PLACE].
	1921	Exchanged rams with CANON'S ASHBY (Sir Alfred Dryden).

CLOUGH HOUSE FARM **Croft, Wainfleet,** **Lincolnshire** *Mrs. P. Caudwell J.P.*	1950	Flock from MILTON. Ram from Miss Bartholomew SAHAM. Sheep to GARROWBY.
	1969	J.S.S. No. 45.
	1989	J.S.S. No. 45.

COGDEN FARM **Burton Bradstock,** **Bridport, Dorset** *R. F. Bailey*	Pre 1967	Sheep from Mr. Burton of North Perrott, so presumably these were ALDON blood.
	1969	J.S.S. No. 90.
	1989	J.S.S. No. 90.

COLES FARM **Box, Wiltshire** *R. Morley*	1963	Listed.

COLESBORNE PARK **Nr. Cheltenham,** **Gloucestershire** *H. J. Elwes, F.R.S. b.1846*	1911	Tried to form Park Sheep Society with Professor J. Cossar Ewart (see p. 29).
	1913	Brought a large collection of his pure-breeds and crosses of Park or Primitive sheep to the Royal Agricultural Show at Bristol. Recognised Old Horned Wiltshire, Norfolk, Shetland, Manx, Soay, Hebridian (now St. Kilda), The Piebald, Black Welsh and Orkney. Exhibited 21 different crosses.

COLDHAYES **East Liss, Hampshire** *Mrs. Frederick Rainsford* *Hannay b. 1888*	1910	'Mrs. Hannay's flock are all two-horned. . . she had 36 from T. Wetherhead of Marlow', who had them from Noble. HN to P.
	1913	Listed. Listed SH. Relationships:- SOMERFORD, HAMMERWOOD, THE CLIFF.

COTSWOLD FARM PARK **Guiting Power, Cheltenham,** **Gloucestershire** *Mr. J. L. Henson*	1969 Sheep from 'Gene Bank' of National Agricultural Centre at Stoneleigh and Reading University. These had originally been at WHIPSNADE ZOO.
	1969 4 ewes and 1 ram from Mr. J. Herdman, Scrubditch, North Cerney, Cirencester, Gloucestershire.
	1970 6 ewes from Miss Pollard [THE DEANERY]. 12 ewes from Captain A. W. Pilkington's dispersal sale. [KING'S WALDEN BURY]. 6 ewes and 1 ram from Reading University Farms, Sonning, Berkshire.
	1989 J.S.S. No. 106.
CRAIGYBIELD **Penicuick, Midlothian,** **North Britain** *Professor J. Cossar Ewart,* *M.D., F.R.S. b.1851*	Pre Had sheep. 1911
	1911 Tried to form Park Sheep Society with H. J. Elwes, F.R.S. (see p. 29).
	1913 Published 'Domestic Sheep and their Wild Ancestors'. Listed SH.
CROMLIX **Dunblane, Perthshire** *Col. A. W. H. Hay-Drummond* *b.1862*	Listed SH.
CROXTON HOUSE **Denby Dale,** **Nr. Huddersfield,** **West Yorkshire** *Mr. F. Bates*	1964 Listed.
CUSWORTH HALL **Doncaster, South Yorkshire** *The Lady Isabella G. K.* *Battie Wrightson b.1855*	c.1898 Rams provided from WENTWORTH WOODHOUSE. -1909
	Pre Had Spanish sheep from same source as Mrs. Farrer's of 1910 INGLEBOROUGH. HN to P.
	1913 36 Ewes. Relationships:- BURGHLEY WESTON, Northamptonshire AVISFORD
DAN-Y-PARK **Crickhowell, South Wales** *Captain R. Sandeman*	1909 Had sheep. HN to P.
DELAPRÉ ABBEY **Northampton,** **Northamptonshire** *Miss M. H. Pleydell-* *Bouverier, O.B.E. b.1865*	1747 Sir Jacob de Bouverie created 1st Viscount Folkestone.
	1934 'Miss Bouverie' bought 20 ewes from Major H. C. C. Batten, D.S.O., M.F.H. [ALDON] arranged by her agent.
THE DEANERY **Bampton, Oxfordshire** *Miss Marjorie Pollard, O.B.E.* *b. c.1899*	Brought her flock from MILTON; the sheep carried very distinctive 'lyre' horns.
	1969 J.S.S. No. 55.
	1970 6 ewes sold to COTSWOLD FARM PARK.

THE DIALSTONE **Hambleton, Thirsk,** **North Yorkshire** *Mrs. B. Hebden*	1964 Listed.
DODFORD **Bromsgrove, Worcestershire** *'Craven, Esq'., P. A. Birch*	1881 'Craven, Esq.' had sheep from CANON'S ASHBY. 1964 P. A. Birch listed.
DODFORD **Weedon Beck, Daventry,** **Warwickshire** *'Craven, Esq'.*	1881 Mentioned as having sheep by Sir H. Dryden [CANON'S ASHBY] writing to Admiral Purefoy, [SHALSTONE MANOR].

DRAYCOT PARK **Cerne, Nr. Chippenham,** **Wiltshire** *The Countess Cowley, b.1866*	c.1879 About 30 sheep, said to have been imported from Zululand. They were wholly black with the exception of the tails and faces. HN 3 and 4.
	1887 Gave a ram and a ewe to Mr. C. Lowndes [CASTLE COMBE]. HN p. 15.
	c.1892 Prince Hatzfeldt gave Mr. Lowndes 2 rams, 'were all black or nearly so, with only the face, tail and a leg or two white, they never had more than two horns'. HN p. 15. In Heatley Noble's article he mentions Prince Hatzfeldt as having sheep at DRAYCOT. Lord Cowley's uncle, Colonel Frederick Arthur Wellesley (b.1844) was 1st Secretary to H. M. Embassy in Austria, and Military Attaché in Russia. Prince Hatzfeldt's father was Ambassador at Vienna 1822-1827 where he died.
	1908 Listed by Richard Lydekker in his 'Guide to Domesticated Animals.' p. 21. Relationships:- TATTON, THORESBY, MANVERS PIERREPONT

THE DUDLEY **ZOOLOGICAL SOCIETY** **Ltd., Dudley, Worcestershire** *(The Earl of Dudley, b.1910)*	1938 Letter from Mr. T. Watson, The Earl of Dudley's Estate Offices, to Mrs. Batten [ALDON]:- 'How are your Jacob sheep ! I ask this because we want to stock some of the paddocks on the castle slopes of the Dudley Zoo ? I thought perhaps some Jacob sheep would be good. As far as I remember they are black and white. . .'
	1938 6 Ewes and 9 Lambs @ £40 from Aldon.
	c.1965 1 Ewe bought from Author — named 'Araminta'.

DUNGAVEL **Strathaven, Lanarkshire,** **Scotland** *The Duke of Hamilton, b.1845*	Pre 1908 Richard Lydekker in his 'Guide to Domesticated Animals' p. 21:- 'The late Duke of Hamilton also possessed a flock in Scotland.' Lydekker describes the sheep thus:- 'A most important characteristic is that the horns, whether two or four, are invariably black. The fleece and tail are long; and while the middle of the face is white, the rest of the head and body is generally piebald. Wholly black specimens are, however, by no means uncommon.' He then lists those who have 'sheep of this breed':- CHATSWORTH, CASTLE COMBE, RAINWORTH, DRAYCOT PARK, INGLEBOROUGH, CANON'S ASHBY, and GORDDINOG.

DUNSTALL HALL
Burton-upon-Trent,
Staffordshire

Sir Reginald Hardy, Bt.
b.1848

After marriage in 1876 moved
to BOWDEN PARK

Listed by SH at DUNSTALL.

c.1883 Sheep from Sir Henry Dryden [CANON'S ASHBY].

1913 14-15 ewes. HN p. 12.

EAST COOMBESHEAD
FARM, Hartford,
Ivybridge, Devon

Mrs. A. A. Matthews

1967 Had two ewes from Mr. D. M. Griffiths, J.S.S. No. 256. Later bought 2 Rams from Miss Helen Hamilton [WHITEHOPE].

1969 J.S.S. No. 24.

1989 J.S.S. No. 24.

EDGECOTE
Nr. Banbury, Oxfordshire

Mr. Cartwright

1840 Sold all sheep to Sir Henry Dryden [CANON'S ASHBY].
-1881

EGLINGHAM HALL
Alnwick, Northumberland

Lt. Col. H. Roland Milvain
M.F.H. b.1880
Colonel Enderby

1953 Listed.

1969 Mrs. Bewicke had the flock: J.S.S. No. 49.

c.1966 Supplied WHITEHOPE with sheep.

ELSENHAM HALL
Bishop's Stortford,
Hertfordshire

Sir Walter Gilbey Bt. b.1831

Past President of the Royal Agricultural Society of England. Past President of Smithfield Club.

Original flock from Colonel Sir George Maude, K.C.B.; Crown Equerry to Queen Victoria [HAMPTON COURT PADDOCKS].

1894 Small crossbred flock.

1896 Gave 3 sheep to Mr. Barker (Sir John) of GRANGE PARK.
According to article in the 'Field' of 23.7.1910 this original stock came from Syria via Colonel Maude. His daughter-in-law, Mrs. Maude, writing to Mr. Heatley Noble maintains 'The sheep you mention were (I think two ewes and a ram) given to Sir George Maude by the late Lord Bradford [WESTON]. . . My husband, on the death of his father in 1894, sold them. I do not know who bought them; of course they had increased, but I do not know how many there were to sell. By their markings they were called "Jacob's Flock"'. In a later letter she adds 'I remember the sheep arriving and being given by the late Lord Bradford, who was Master of the Horse to Sir George Maude.'
Sir Walter Gilbey's Agent, Mr. Burrell wrote:- 'Sir Walter Gilbey bought the Syrian sheep originally from Sir George Maude, but where Sir George got them from Sir Walter does not know.' HN p. 5.

1913 Listed.
Relationship:- GRANGE PARK.

ETTINGTON
Stratford-on-Avon,
Warwickshire

Mr. William Gibbins

c.1881 Sheep from CHARLECOTE.

c.1891 Supplied Mr. Smith-Rylands [BARFORD] with ewes.

1913 30 ewes kept for breeding. HN p. 13/14.
Presented Mr. Foster, M.P. [CANWELL HALL] with flock of 10 ewes.
This transaction mentioned by HN to P uses 'P. S. Foster, M.P.'

EYREFIELD LODGE
Curagh Camp, Co. Kildare,
Ireland

Major Giles H. Loder, M.C.
b.1884

1910 Had sheep. HN to P.
Relationships:-
Sir Robert Loder 1823-1888 had 8 sons and 2 daughters.
1st son, see LEONARDSLEA.
2nd son is Major Giles.
6th son, see MAIDWELL HALL and
WEST HASLERTON HALL.
1st daughter, see KNEPP.
8th son KILDARE

FARLEIGH WALLOP
Basingstoke, Hampshire

The Earl of Portsmouth
b.1898

1953 Listed.

FAY GATE HOUSE
Crawley, Sussex

Sir Claud Alexander Bt.
b.1867

Pre Ram to COLESBOURNE PARK illustrated in 'Guide to Primitive
1913 Breeds of Sheep' by Elwes.
Listed SH.

FEARN FARM
Alexton, Uppingham,
Rutland

R. T. Clarke

1963 Listed.

FLOODGATES
Horsham, Sussex

Sir Merrik Burrell Bt. C.B.E.
b.1877

1887 30 ewes from Sir Robert Loder [LEONARDSLEA], which had
come from Sir Henry Dryden [CANON'S ASHBY] before 1881.

c.1907 12 ewes from Major E. Loder [EYREFIELD LODGE].
HN p. 12.

1913 Listed 30 ewes.

1913 20 ewes to R. B. Loder [LYVEDEN].

1936 Photograph in Daily Mirror of April 15th of some 15 ewes and
lambs.

1953 Listed.
Relationships:- KNEPP, CANON'S ASHBY, EYREFIELD,
MAIDWELL, WEST HASLERTON.

GARROWBY
Buckthorpe, York,
North Yorkshire

Sir Francis Lindley Wood, Bt.
b.1771

Viscount Halifax, b.1912

1771 Lord Halifax maintained his great, great grandfather had sheep.
-1846

1879 Grandson of Sir Francis, Lt. Colonel H. J. Lindley
[BRODSWORTH] b.1843, fought in the Zulu War.

1905 Brother of above took name of Meynell [HOAR CROSS].

1964 Listed.

Pre Ram from author [THE KNOLL FARM].
1969

1969 J.S.S. No. 13.

1978 2nd President of the Jacob Sheep Society. Flock of 25 ewes
-80 and lambs.

1989 J.S.S. No. 13
Relationship:- BRODSWORTH.

GARSCUBE
Bearsden, Glasgow,
Stirlingshire, Scotland

Lady Campbell of Succoth
b. c.1858

1909   Letter from Estate Office to Colonel Platt (GORDDINOG) to his Scottish Estate, Grennards:-

'I understand that you keep a flock of the Black and White African Sheep and Sir Archibald and Lady Campbell of Succoth, for whom I act as Estate Factor, have asked me to write to you on the subject of a young ram for this autumn's service. Lady Campbell having heard from her sister Mrs. Farrer, that you were in Scotland, wondered whether you would be passing through Glasgow on your way south and could take a run out to Garscube to see her sheep. There are 22 ewes, most of which came from Mrs. Farrer and we want some fresh blood. . . Can you tell me if the true type has 4 horns, or whether this peculiarity is the result of inbreeding? Some of our ewes have 4 horns, but most only 2 and some, which I am drafting out, have no horns at all. I want a ram with 4 horns, as this will probably help to establish the 4 horned type. I understand that Mrs. Farrer has used a Syrian ram, but surely this is departing from the true breed and getting a cross.'

1910   Flock already in being; letter from Estate Office to Sir A. Dryden [CANON'S ASHBY]:-

'I understand you keep a flock of four horned Black and White sheep and as we have two ram lambs with four horns to sell this season from the Garscube flock, I thought you would pardon my writing to ask whether you would care to purchase one or both of them. These rams are by a very nice looking ram which I brought . . . last year from Colonel Platt and they are very typical of the breed.

I have a fine big 4 year old tup, but he only has 2 horns and seems to be of a different type from the ewes.

I shall be very grateful to you for any information you can give me and if you will let me know whether you have a young ram with 4 horns and not crossed in any way, which you could sell to us and its price.'

1913   Listed as a small flock.

Relationships:- INGLEBOROUGH, AVISFORD.

GISBURN PARK
Clitheroe, Yorkshire
[Lancashire]

Sir Thomas Lister
® Lord Ribblesdale) b. c.1743

The illustration, 'Skull of a Species of Sheep formerly kept at Gisburn Park' From T. D. Whitaker's 'The History and Antiquities of The Deanery of Craven' is undated (see page 24).

It is known that several different animals were kept by Lord Ribblesdale including 'Wild Cattle', the stuffed heads of which hung in the kitchen. Some of these skulls and heads went to the Totlord Museum, Settle, and may now be held by the North Craven Heritage Trust.

GLYNDE
Lewes, Sussex

(Viscount Hampden)
A tenant farmer

1953   Listed.

1964   Listed.

GORDDINOG
Llanfairfechen, Caernarvon,
North Wales

Colonel Henry Platt C.B.
b. c.1841

His brother Fredrick's sons
were Eric and Alfred

also

GRENNARDS
Ardgay, Rosshire, Scotland

Letters between Colonel Platt and Mr. Heatley Noble were saved by Professor R. T. White of Bangor University who gave them to the Head of the Agricultural Department, Mr. Gwynne Williams B.Sc. who in turn gave them to Mrs. Lloyd Jones (J.S.S. No. 691). See page 35.

Origin of flock from Mr. (Alexander ?) McCorquodale [LANSADURN]. HN p. 14 & SH.

1908   Listed by Richard Lydekker in his 'Guide to Domesticated Animals.' p. 21.

1908   Ram from WENTWORTH WOODHOUSE, son of CHATSWORTH ram. Ref. Sir Arthur Dryden to TABLEY.

1909   Colonel Platt invited to GARSCUBE to see sheep.

1909   Heatley Noble asking Platt for ram to be sent to TEMPLE COMBE.

1910   Offered to exchange 4 shear Ram with WELBECK.

1913   40 ewes listed.

Note: Mr. Norman McCorquodale of WINSLOW HALL may be son of above, as in 1913 had 'a small number, descendants of his father's flock.' HN p. 1.

Listed SH.

GOURD FARM
Compton Abbas, Dorset

J. & R. Hardings

1953   Illustration in the Farmer and Stockbreeder, showing a flock of Jacobs with the caption:- 'Black-and-white sheep on a West Country Farm are an unusual sight in this country. These are part of a flock of South African or Jacob's Sheep. . . the lambs are the result of using a Dorset Horn Ram. It has been found that the sheep can look after themselves with little or no extra feed.'

XXVII. GRANGE PARK
'The Field' 23rd July 1910

THE GRANGE
Bishop's Stortford,
Hertfordshire

Sir John Barker Bt. b.1840

c.1899   This flock was established some sixteen years ago at The Grange . . . from foundation stock procured from the late Sir Walter Gilbey's flock at ELSENHAM. The Elsenham flock had been purchased

c.1879   about twenty years earlier from the late Colonel Maude, who resided at Hampton Court Paddocks for many years, in charge of The Royal Thoroughbred Stud then kept there, and who had imported the sheep from Syria. HN p. 10.

1912   Writing to Colonel Platt, Mr. Heatley Noble says:-

'I wish I could get you to believe that neither Mrs. Farrer's ram nor Sir John Barker's ewe had anything to do with Syria! I have proved this beyond the very slightest possibility of doubt. The late Colonel Maude got them from the late Lord Bradford not Syria. Lord Bradford got his from Fitzwilliam. Colonel Maude sold his flock to Sir W. Gilbey, the latter some to Sir John Barker, Sir John to Mrs. Farrer. They never came from Syria and all that story is a *mistake*. As I can prove by letters I have from the present Mrs. Maude who well remembers their arrival and the donor was Lord Bradford.'

1910   In the July 23rd edition of The Field, The Country Gentlemen's Newspaper, p. 203 'The quantity of milk given by these sheep has not been measured, but it must be large, and if ever the custom of keeping milk sheep, which is so common on the other side of the North Sea, should be adopted in this country, Sir John Barker's strain might be well worth drawing upon. A sheep is a much more manageable creature than a goat, and there is the yield of wool as well as the lambs and milk.

1913   A small flock listed.

1915 Dispersal Sale.

Being Past President and Member of the Council of the Polo Pony Society, Messrs Tattersall of Knightsbridge London took the sale of 'The Grange Flock of Syrian Sheep. The property of the late Sir John Barker, was auctioned on Friday, 16th April 1915, followed by a sale of his ponies.

According to the catalogue:-

The Syrian sheep are extensively bred for milch purposes in South-Eastern Europe and Asia Minor. They are very prolific, as the ewes often lamb twice a year, namely, in the spring and in the autumn. Twelve ewes have produced forty lambs in one year, i.e. twenty-one in the spring and nineteen in the autumn; one ewe had two lots of three lambs in the one year, and another ewe two families of two lambs in the year — all living. A remarkable record of ten lambs from two ewes in one year.

They are wonderfully hardy and free from disease, as they have been pastured on the same piece of land at Bishops Stortford for the whole sixteen years, and not one has suffered from footrot. The ewes yield from three to four pints of rich milk per day, enough to supply a small household, and in flavour the milk resembles that of the cow. They also produce very good mutton; equal to that of any short wool sheep.

The Syrian sheep will appeal to lovers of animals, either for the production of milk and mutton or as suitable for the Home Park, for in a remarkable degree they combine utilitarian and picturesque properties. The rams are particularly attractive, as their four horns are much larger than those of the ewes.

The flock, which at present consists of about thirty head, comprising four rams, twenty-two ewes, one wether, and this season's crop of lambs, will be sold by Messrs. Tattersall, immediately after the sale of the Polo Pony stud. The rams will be sold singly and the ewes in couples with their lambs.

	Result of Sale	£. s. d.
1. 1 Ram (2 shear)	W. Balding	2. 0. 0.
2. 1 Shearling ram	Alfd. Mansell & Co.	12. 0. 0.
3. 1 Ram lamb	R. G. Baty	2. 7. 0.
4. 1 Ram lamb	Lady Egerton of Tatton	2. 11. 0.
5. 2 Ewes, 3 Lambs	F. Banks	5. 2. 0.
6. 2 Ewes, 3 Lambs	Alfd. Mansell & Co.	11. 0. 0.
7. 2 Ewes, 4 Lambs	W. Balding	10. 0. 0.
8. 2 Ewes, 3 Lambs	W. Balding	13. 5. 0.
9. 2 Ewes, 3 Lambs	Capt. C. S. Schreiber	16. 15. 0.
10. 2 Ewes, 3 Lambs	W. Balding	16. 5. 0.
11. 2 Ewes, 3 Lambs	W. Balding	17. 0. 0.
12. 2 Ewes, 3 Lambs	W. Balding	5. 15. 0.
13. 1 Ewe, 2 Autumn Lambs (1 Ewe, 1 Wether)	A. G. Watney	13. 0. 0.
14. 2 Ewes, 1 Lamb	Alfd. Mansell & Co.	18. 0. 0.
15. 2 Ewes, 2 Lambs	W. Balding	10. 10. 0.

At the time of printing some ewes had not lambed.

Note: No. 9 see MARLESFORD HALL.

Relationship:- ELSENHAM HALL

SYRIAN EWE AND LAMBS.
THE PROPERTY OF SIR JOHN BARKER.

XXVIII.

GREAT GLEMHAM HOUSE, Saxmundham, Suffolk

The Earl of Cranbrooke
b.1900

1953 Letter from The Old House, Withnell Fold, Chorley, Lancashire:-

'Many thanks for your letter of the 15th. I am most grateful for the particulars you have given me regarding your flock of Spanish sheep.

It is rather extraordinary how this breed, crossed with others should invariably produce black progeny. I am told, however, that crossed with the Dorset Horn the lambs are spotted.

.... On the reverse I have jotted down a few owners of Jacob's sheep as requested'.

Note: The 10 flocks listed have been used for the '1953 Listed' information.

1963 Listed.
Relationship:- DUNSTALL

HAMMERWOOD HOUSE
Iping, Nr. Midhurst, Sussex

John Lakin Esq., b.1910

1964 Listed.
Relationships:- THE CLIFF, KNEPP.

HAMPTON COURT PADDOCKS
Molesey, Middlesex

Sir George Maude K.C.B. b.1817

1882 or 1884 Had sheep from the Earl of Bradford [WESTON].

1894 Sold small flock to Sir Walter Gilbey [ELSINGHAM].

1910 An article in 'The Field' of 23rd July states that the origin of these sheep came from Syria to go on to Sir Walter Gilbey. This is refuted by Sir George's daughter-in-law who remembers 'I think two ewes and a ram' being given by the late Lord Bradford. 'By their markings they were called "Jacob's Flock"'. HN p. 5.

Note: Lord Bradford was related to Sir George, and was a contempory in age; Master of Horse 1874-1880, and again in 1885-1886, whilst Sir George was Crown Equerry to Queen Victoria 1817-1894 — this seems a more likely story. But 'Syria' remains a mystery.
Relationships:- MILTON, WESTON.

HASSOP
Baslow, Derbyshire

Mr. Francis Eyre (Wife b.1732)

1762 'To Mr. Eyre's Keeper for eight spotted lambs sent to his Grace for £1. 1s. 0d.' (CHATSWORTH Account Book 1757-60) p. 61; ref; 1762.)

Note: Francis Eyre of Warkworth succeeded to Hassop Estate in 1792 upon death of his nephew.

HAZELWOOD CASTLE
Tadcaster, North Yorkshire

Sir William Vavasour Bt. b.1846

1909 Listed. HN to P.

1910 Writing to Colonel Platt again, Mr. Heatley Noble says:-
'It might be as well to trace the flock once owned by Vavasour, I think this would make my list complete.
.... Questions I would like asked re Vavasour's flock:-
Origin of acquisition? Date? No. of ewes kept for breeding. Any further particulars?
Relationships:- LULWORTH CASTLE, BRAMHAM PARK, ALLERTON.

Near High Wycombe, Buckinghamshire

Mr. Robert Vaughan

1913 25 Ewes listed, which were purchased in Warwickshire; originally two-horned, now most of the rams carry four. HN p. 15 & 16.

Pre 1932 Notice from The Times of 22nd April, 1933:-
'Another very striking race of domestic animals to be seen at Whipsnade [Zoo] is the flock of piebald sheep in the paddock. . . The sheep were bought last year from the estate of Mr. Robert Vaughan near High Wycombe, where they had been for many years. They have thrived at Whipsnade and there are at present over a dozen lambs. The sheep are rather tall, with curly wool, and are mottled black and white, with a white blaze on the forehead. The rams tend to have four horns. They are generally known as Spanish sheep, and there are small flocks of them on several private estates in England. There is, however, little evidence of their origin.'

HIGHFIELD **Shrewsbury, Shropshire** *T. Middleton Howells*	c.1881 Original stock from CHATSWORTH. HN p. 9. 1910 Had sheep. HN to P. 1913 Listed: 18-20 Ewes.
HIGHGATES FARM RR7 **St. Mary's, Ontario,** **Canada, NOM 2VO** *Mr. & Mrs. J. M. Ridley*	1969 Started flock with stock from Assiniboine Park Zoo, whose stock originated from Whipsnade Zoo. Known as 'Scottish Four-Horned Sheep.' (1978 Letter to J.S.S. Sec.) Ex J.S.S. No. 601.
HOAR CROSS **Burton-on-Trent,** **Staffordshire** *Sir F. G. L. Meynell Bt.* *b.1846* *Lt. Col. F. H. L. Meynell* *D.S.O., b.1880*	1909 'The last cross I got was from Mr. Meynell of Hoar Cross, but the Ram was much too dark — very little spotted. . .' HN to P. Note: Lt. Colonel H. J. L. Wood 1843-1903 (brother of F. G. L. M.) was in Zulu War 1879. Relationships:- THORP MANDERVILLE, KNOCKER, LOCOCK, GARROWBY, WESTON, Northamptonshire.
HOLME PIERREPONT **Nottingham,** **Nottinghamshire** *The Earl Manvers, Baron* *Pierrepont of Holme* *Pierrepont, b.1888*	See THORESBY PARK. Ref. J.S.S. No. 2792. Relationship:- TATTON
HOLYWELL **Swanmore, Hampshire** *M. Portal* 	1920 According to oldest inhabitant of Soberton (via J.S.S. No. 193) there were 'peculiar sheep' at Holywell. 1923 Writing to Eric Platt [GORDDINOG]. 'I see you state the horns of your Ram come forward and not back — some do I know (Sir W. Cooke's do) [WYLD COURT] I rather wonder if someone did not use a St. Kilda Ram at one time. . . A Mrs. Farrer [INGLEBOROUGH] wrote me hers came from the Cape when Hely Hutchinson was out there in about 1840 I fancy — he got 6 given in exchange for a piano — which sounds circumstantial evidence — another writes theirs came from Portugal — another writes their father or grandfather used to get a fresh Ram from Spain. Another that theirs came from Palestine or Syria originally. If they are all correct then the pedigree is a mixture of the Spotted or Ringstraked sheep of the Bible, which you see on Judaen hills now — or in lower Lebanon range crossed with the Afrikander sheep; the North African sheep (the Moors left some in Spain when they retired, at the same time as they left Camels behind, which still breed & roam wild there) and I daresay one might add a cross or so of Highland sheep and St. Kilda. Spain is probably the one place where they are not. To my mind the curious feature is their throwing black lambs at birth, with white tip to tail and white star between ears or in front of, if crossed with a domestic sheep. I do not know origin of your Welsh Sheep but anyrate, it is hardy if its the wild black sheep I used to see at Lord Powys' place Walcot when shooting.'
HOOK HOUSE **Brenzett, Romney Marsh,** **Kent** *J. H. Paine*	1963 Listed. 1969 Listed: J.S.S. No. 21 (Poplar Hall).

INGLEBOROUGH
Yorkshire, Via Lancaster
Austwick, Nr. Settle,
North Yorkshire

Mrs. 'Beckie' Farrer b. c.1889

Writing in 1913 Mr. Heatley Noble says:-

c.1815 'Perhaps the most satisfactory history exists in the case of the flock owned by Mrs. Farrer. The original parents of these sheep were brought home from the Cape about a century ago by the present owner's grandfather, Colonel Farrer, who believed that they had been imported into the Cape by Spanish or Portuguese settlers, who were supposed to have brought them from their own country. A portion of this original flock was given to Sir Henry Dryden's ancestor, so the Ingleborough and the Canons Ashby flock have the same ancestors.' (Footnote 'This is a mistake; see note on the two flocks. HN'). HN p. 3.

See HOLYWELL note: 'A Mrs. Farrer wrote me hers came from the Cape when Hely Hutchinson was out there in about 1840 I fancy — he got 6 given in exchange for a piano — which sounds circumstantial evidence.'

1887 The late Mr. C. Lowndes started a flock when he was given a ram and a ewe by the late Countess of Cowley. . . said to have been imported from Zululand. . . wholly black with the exception of the tails and faces, and I believe have little to do with the sheep to which this article refers. They were crossed with piebald sheep. . . from Mrs. Farrer, and others, until in 1908 the flock numbered 400 ewes and lambs.

1908 Listed by Richard Lydekker in his 'Guide to Domesticated Animals.' p. 21.

1909 Writing to Mrs. Farrer, Sir Alfred Dryden says 'I think you are mistaken as to the history of these sheep. . . I don't think Colonel Hutchinson ever brought any of them from the Cape or elsewhere, and Mrs. Packe' [Mrs. Farrer's mother] 'probably got her sheep, which you now have, from my brother's flock here. [See CANON'S ASHBY.] Probably this flock and that of Sir Alfred Dryden have the same origin though the accounts differ somewhat. Mrs. Farrer writes to me, "I may assure you on the authority of my aunts (daughters of Col. the Hon. H. Hely Hutchinson) that the origin of our flock is this: They were sent from the Cape by my Grandfather's military successor there to him soon after his marriage in 1823. The present Sir Alfred Dryden's flock were derived from this. My Grandfather's were in the country before the sheep described by Sir Alfred as having been brought from Spain by an officer's wife. Sir Henry's account differs from that of his successor, Sir Alfred. From my earliest years I was always told my Grandfather gave some to Sir H. Dryden'. HN p. 12.

1909 Letter from Estate Factor, J. Harry Dods at GARSCUBE to Colonel Platt.

'I understand that you keep a flock of the Black & White North African Sheep and Sir Archibald and Lady Campbell of Succoth. . . have asked me to write to you on the subject of a young ram for this autumn's service. Lady Campbell, having heard from her sister Mrs. Farrer, that you were in Scotland. . . could take a run out to Garscube to see her sheep. There are 22 ewes, most of which came from Mrs. Farrer & we want some fresh blood.

I understand that Mrs. Farrer has used a Syrian ram, but surely this is departing from the true breed and getting a cross.'

1913 . . . 'Lady Campbell of Succoth [Mrs. Farrer's sister] has a small flock the same in origin as Mrs. Farrer's. Lady Isabella Battie-Wrightson [CUSWORTH] owns a flock of thirty-six ewes of the same origin as the Ingleborough flock.' HN p. 13.

c.1913 Letter to Sir Arthur Dryden [CANON'S ASHBY]

'Your beautiful ram arrived quite well and we admire him very much. All except his horns which are very handsome but not what we have bred from for some years. I have chosen you one of our two best shearling ewes with two horns and think you will like its form and markings. Thank you so much for the exchange which comes at such a timely moment for us. If you should hear of anyone wishing to start a flock of these sheep do remember me for I could quite spare 6 ewes and 6 or more lambs. My man says we are overcrowded. Your sheep starts I believe tomorrow?'

1913 'The ram lamb under the X was sent to CANON'S ASHBY on 18th August 1913 by Mrs. Farrer in exchange for a ewe lamb from the flock at Canon's Ashby, but died before it could be used.' See CANON'S ASHBY illustrations.

1913 Listed. 16 ewes.

1923 See HOLYWELL

Relationships:- AVISFORD, GARSCUBE, CUSWORTH, WESTON, Northamptonshire

INWOOD
Templecombe, Somerset
Miss Guest

1953 Listed.

KILKENNY CASTLE
Kilkenny, Co. Tipperary,
Ireland
Lady Constance Butler b.1879

1903 Original stock from WENTWORTH WOODHOUSE (Fitzwilliam).

1910 Listed HN to P.

1913 Had 6 breeding ewes.

Relationships:- SHANBALLY CASTLE, MILTON, CHATSWORTH

KING'S WALDEN BURY
Offley, Nr. Hitchen,
Hertfordshire
Major J. F. Harrison b. c.1883

Captain A. W. Pilkington M.C., b.1898

Captain L. C. Vaughan – Estate Manager

Mr. Edgar Field – Accountant

Pre When Mr. Edgar Field appointed Accountant, the sheep were
1910 there when he arrived.

Major Harrison's daughters remember pied sheep in the park from early childhood.

1953 Listed as belonging to L. C. Vaughan of King's Walden – presumably 'Captain Vaughan' the Estate Manager.

1955 Two Shearling ewes to RAVENDALE, J.S.S. No. 16.

1953 Sheep to SCALFORD HALL.
-70

1969 J.S.S. No. 11 'Pilkington Farms.'

1970 'Pilkington Dispersal Sale' 12 ewes bought by COTSWOLD FARM PARK.

KIRKLAND OF GELSTON
Gelston, Castle Douglas,
Kirkcudbrightshire,
Scotland
Miss K. M. A. Clark

1963 Listed.

1967 2 or 3 in-lamb ewes to KNOCKCROON.

1969 J.S.S. No. 38 with 90 sheep at ORROLAND, Dundrennan, Kirkcudbrightshire.

KNEPP CASTLE
West Grinstead, Sussex
Sir Merrik Burrell Bart. b.1877

In an article from The Estate Magazine dated July 1936 entitled 'Jacob's Sheep' the following are extracts:-

'Strangely, the breed, though a foreign variety, has been peculiar only to England for at least five centuries, and perhaps for a much longer period. Recently it was reported to be extinct. . . owned by Sir Merrik Burrel, Bart., this year's President of the Royal Agricultural Society. . . they roam the pastures of his Knepp Castle estate. . . . They are said to have originated in the Holy Land as long as 3,000 years ago and are believed to be the identical breed (the spotted, speckled and ring-streaked) which Jacob received from his Uncle Laban in return for his services.

[It] is the largest flock, and the most typical. . . thriving where other sheep succumb to hunger and the vicissitudes of the weather.

1899 Sir Merrik Burrell inherited his herd on succeeding to the title and Knepp Castle estate some years ago, his predecessor having acquired them from a distant relative and friend, Sir Henry Dryden [CANON'S ASHBY] more than half a century ago.

. . . The sheep resemble a deer and goat cross. The creatures are white, profusely splashed with black; and are horned, and resemble deer in their movements and build. The breed is noted for milk yielded by the ewe, and sweet, lean mutton. Once the custom was to kill and eat a selection of the lambs (generally twins or triplets) or to rear them on cows' milk, and to use the milk of the sheep mothers for household purposes. The delicacy, the richness and the delicious flavour of milk and flesh alike are beyond dispute. They will not fatten as will the Southdown and our other commercial breeds because of their restless nature; and though their wool is superior to all other for hand spinning and weaving, is not suitable for spinning and weaving by mechanical means. . . . no attempt has ever been made to popularise them or save the breed from ultimate extinction.'

Extracts from the September issue of the same magazine follows:-

'Sir — I would suggest that there may be far more flocks of Jacob's Sheep than Mr. J. C. Bristow-Noble thinks. I have a letter from the late Mr. Heatley Noble, saying he knew of over fifty flocks — and probably there were many more. One feels sure that many people would keep some if. . . the local butcher were the buyer. . . and control could be made over their habit of getting out of any field — if they want to. . . They are so attractive to the eye and so very hardy. Their origin in this country Mr. Heatley Noble could not discover. . .

There were three flocks in France in 1925, and rams were sent out from Great Britain for change of blood.

[Signed] Spotted Sheep.'

Note: If anyone knows details of the three French flocks, or of the exportations, please let the author know.

An undated illustration appeared in the Daily Express at much the same time as identical wording is used.

1913 30 Ewes listed at FLOODGATES (Residence).

1953 Listed, FLOODGATES.

1964 Listed, KNEPP.

1969 J.S.S No. 15. The Hon. Lady Burrell.

1989 J.S.S. No. 15.
     Relationships:- LEONARDSLEA, CANON'S ASHBY,
                 EYREFIELD, MAIDWELL,
                 WEST HASLERTON.

KNOCKCROON
Barrhill, Girvan, Ayrshire,
Scotland

Mrs. M. Morren

1967 Saw a picture of Jacobs in the 'Scottish Farmer' and asked her husband to give her some for a birthday present. These were 2 or 3 ewes-in-lamb from Miss K. M. A. Clark Ex. J.S.S. No. 38.
     Tup on loan from Mr. Jack Marshall. Had stock from Mr. John Young J.S.S. No. 866. He has had stock from Knockcroon.

1969 J.S.S Member No. 98.
     Sold as a flock to 'Pheobie Stewart of Newton Stewart'.

1989 J.S.S. No. 98.

KNOCKMARK **Drumrie, Co. Meath, Ireland** *J. B. Donnelly*	c.1902	8 or 10 ewes from Mr. McCorquodale (LANSADURN). HN p. 14.
	1910	Listed.
	1913	Listed.

THE KNOLL FARM **Aldington, Nr. Ashford, Kent** *The Lady Aldington*	1960	Given a stock ewe lamb by Mrs. A. R. Pym (BARNFIELD).
	1964	Used ram from Wales at Barnfield.
	1964	A Ram called 'Harold' born on election day sold to ARLINGTON.
	1965	Had ewe from LITTLE GAINS.
	c.1965	Ewe 'Araminta' to DUDLEY ZOO.
	1967	Ram from KNEPP.
	c.1968	Ram to GARROWBY.
	1969	Ram from Brogues Wood Farms Ltd. Tenterden.
	1969	Founder member J.S.S. No. 2.
	1989	J.S.S. No. 2. See inside back cover illustration.

LANSADURN **Anglesea** *Mr. McCorquodale* *Sons: Alec McCorquodale,* *Norman McCorquodale of* *Winslow Hall,* *Buckinghamshire*	c.1902	Sold sheep to Mr. J. B. Donnelly, by 1913, 8-10 ewes. HN p. 14.
	1909	Writing to Colonel Platt, Mr. Heatley Noble says: 'I wrote to Alec McCorquodale who I know well, he tells me he has no sheep now, his father had a flock which were sold'. Note: It may have been a son of Norman who became Lord McCorquodale to live at COTSWOLD PARK. Relationship:- WINSLOW.

LEONARDSLEA **Horsham, Sussex** *Captain Sir Robert Loder Bt.* *b.1823* *Sir Edmund Loder Bt.* *b.1849*		Sir Robert Loder had sheep from Dryden [CANON'S ASHBY] probably from CHATSWORTH.
	Pre 1881	Flock from Canon's Ashby (Sir Henry Dryden). HN p. 12.
	1887	Some to Sir Merrick Burrel [FLOODGATES]. HN p. 12.
	1913	Listed. Relationships:- EYREFIELD, MAIDWELL, WEST HASLERTON, KNEPP.

LITTLE GAINS FARM **Aldington, Nr. Ashford, Kent** *Mrs. Gladys Calthorpe*	c.1956	Had sheep from SISSINGHURST.
	1964	Sold one ewe to THE KNOLL FARM.
	c.1968	Disposed of small flock.

LITTLE GLEMHAM **Saxmundham, Suffolk** *The Lady Blanche Cobbold* *b.1898*		Probably brought her sheep from CHATSWORTH.
	c.1967	Used to exchange Rams with GREAT GLEMHAM HOUSE.
	1969	J.S.S. No. 48.
	1989	Captain P. M. Cobbold J.S.S. No. 48. Relationship:- CHATSWORTH.

LOWOOD **Melrose, Roxburghshire** *Miss Hamilton* **WHITEHOPE** **Innerleithen, Peebleshire** *Miss H. B. Hamilton*	1965	Listed at Lowood.
	1969	J.S.S. No. 63. With 102 sheep.
	1989	J.S.S. No. 63. *SEE WHITE HOPE* Relationship:- SKENE HOUSE

LULWORTH CASTLE
Wareham, Dorset

Colonel Sir Joseph Weld
O.B.E.

LULWORTH CASTLE
FARMS LTD.

C. G. Hyde

c.1964 Had sheep via Mr. C. G. Hyde from ALDON.

1969 J.S.S. No. 31 with 61 sheep.

Note: Of interest is that Colonel M. C. Weld wrote an introduction to William Youatt's 'Sheep; Their Management and Diseases' which was republished 1891. (See pp. 14 & 18) Also that Herbert Weld, in 1899 brought back many new species of animals for the British Museum of Natural History.

Relationship:- HAZLEWOOD CASTLE.

LYVEDEN
Corby, Northamptonshire

The Lord Lyveden, b.1892

Listed by SH.

Relationship:- SUDBURY HALL.

MAIDWELL HALL
Lamport, Northamptonshire

R. B. Loder, b.1864

1910 Had sheep. HN to P.

1913 20 ewes from Sir Merrik Burrell [FLOODGATES]. HN p. 13.

Relationships:- EYREFIELD,
HASLERTON HALL
(WEST HASLERTON HALL)
LEONARDSLEA

THE MANOR
Wootton Fitzpaine,
Nr. Bridport, Dorset

Mr. and Mrs. A. D. Pass
Mrs. K. E. Fortescue

c.1946 Owned flock.

1973 Writing to the author Mrs. Fortescue says:-

'I have inherited a tiny flock of Jacob Sheep, had from the stock of Colonel Weld of Chideock. When my mother bought her first three ewes they were in lamb to some sort of Down ram and produced six black lambs. There was only one ewe, which we kept, and her wool has proved very attractive to our spinning ladies, who say moreover that black wool is hard to get. I wish to reproduce this cross, but Colonel Weld disclaims all knowledge of it and my mother is dead. Will any Down ram produce blacks on a Jacob? Or was it a genetic oddity of one . . . I have just joined the Jacob Sheep Society. . . with about 10 ewes.'

1989 J.S.S. No. 363 of Knapp Farm, Wootton Fitzpaine.

MANOR FARM
Wool, Dorset

C. G. Hyde

Pre From Colonel H. C. C. Batten D.S.O. [ALDON].
1964 Some go to LULWORTH CASTLE.

1969 J.S.S. No. 31.

1989 J.S.S. No. 1575.

MARINO
Nr. Dublin, Co. Cork,
Ireland

James, 4th Viscount and
1st Earl Charlemont, b.1728

21 Apr A charming letter from the local Member of Parliament,
1786 Sir Edward Newenham (1732-1814):-

'My Lord, I flatter myself that I shall send you a real Curiosity; about 14 years ago Mr. Dalrymple sent me from Tartary, a few seeds of the real Rhubarb. . .'

he then goes on to say to whom he had given seeds, and after a page of instructions says:-

'. . . let your Gardener, just Crack the pot, after he puts it into the Ground, and next year he can take the broken parts away – as it is near flowering, great Care is Necessary – your Lambs have been all the Evening in the Library, & made the Lapdogs give way, by butting them – I have this evening got 2 of the Black Hiccory, & Butter Nutts trees from Colonel Wadsworth of Connecticut; if they live until September, your Lordship shall have half of them.'

Ref: Royal Irish Academy No. 12 R 14 No. 65.

3 Jul 1787   from John Wesley's Journal:-

'Tues. 3. – A few friends took me to Marino, a seat of Lord Charlemont's, four miles from Dublin. It contains a lovely mixture of wood, water and lawns, on which are several kinds of foreign sheep, with great plenty of peacocks; but I could not hear any singing-birds of any kind.'

Pre 1791   'Tour through Ireland' by Charles Topham Bowden, published in Dublin 1791.

'Marino, the seat of Lord Charlemont. This is one of the most beautiful and elegant seats in the world, happily situated, and in a demesne improved in the highest taste, comprehending 238 acres, laid out in plantations – sheepwalks – lawns and delightful park. There are sheep here with four, six and eight horns.'

Note: 'Lord Charlemont's Travels in Greece and Turkey 1749' by the late Professor W. B. Stanford and E. J. Finopoulus have been published recently.

The letters gives a wonderful picture of these enthusiasts who collect rare plants and animals from around the world to grace their menageries and parks, fore runners of Zoological Collections and Breed Societies.

MARLESFORD HALL
Wickham Market, Suffolk

Captain Charles Shuldham Schreiber, b. c.1873

1915   At GRANGE PARK sale bought 2 Ewes and 3 Lambs for £16. 15. 0.

Relationships:- KINGS WALDEN, POWIS CASTLE.

Marlow, Buckinghamshire

T. Wetherhead

1913   Bought 36 ewes from Heatley Noble which were sold to Mrs. Hannay [COLDHAYES]. HN p. 11.

MAWBIE MAINS
Annan, Dumfrieshire,
VIOLETBANK HOUSE

Mrs. Ella Maxwell

1949   Bought a British Fresian Bull calf at 'mad price' from Frank Loftus J.S.S. No. 54; the Luck Pennies were two ewe lambs. Mr. Loftus told Mrs. Maxwell that some of his flock had come from Cambridge University.

Had stock from WHITEHOPE, at the time the only lamb Miss Hamilton had.

1961   Had ram from Mrs. Buist of Kirkbank, Kelso J.S.S. No. 83.

1968   J.S.S. No. 74.

1989   J.S.S. No. 74.

MELBURY HOUSE
Nr. Dorchester, Dorset

The Earl of Ilchester O.B.E. b.1874

1910   Had sheep. HN to P.

c.1940   The ram 'Hartington' from CHATSWORTH; others exchanged between the two estates.

1958 -64   A few Jacobs at Melbury.

1964   Listed. (The Strangeways Estate Ltd.)

74 MIDDLE ROAD
Saintfield, Co. Down

Mr. Derek McMillan

1973   Writing to the author Lord Dunleath says:-

I have discovered that Mr. Derek McMillan. . . has seven ewes and three rams. His father having bought the first ram and ewe from here [BALLYWALTER]'

1989   J.S.S. No. 608.

MIDDLETON TOWER
King's Lynn, Norfolk

T. H. Barclay

1964   Listed.

MILL BROW FARM
Loughrigg, Ambleside,
Westmorland
Miss A. Wood

1966   Bought five Ewes from Mr. Slack of Brougham Castle Farm.

c.1968 Bought a Ewe from a farm near Kendal.
        Bought a ram from SHALSTONE.

MILEYDALE
Ellers Brow, Loughrigg,
Ambleside, Cumbria

Messrs. Wood & Hainsworth

1969   J.S.S. No. 73.

1989   J.S.S. No. 73.

XXIX. MILTON 'Farmer & Stockbreeder' July 1910

MILTON
Peterborough,
Northamptonshire

The Earl Fitzwilliam K.G.
b.1815

The Hon. George Fitzwilliam
M.P., b.1817

1851   Supplied rams to CHATSWORTH. HN p. 9.

1870   14 ewes to WESTON [Bradford].
        6 ewes presented by Mr. George Fitzwilliam of Milton to
        J. S. H. Fullerton [NOBLETHORPE HALL]. HN p. 10.

c.1905 25 breeding ewes originally presented by Mr. George Fitzwilliam to
        Mr. R. Swan [ROCKCLIFFE PARK]. HN p. 10.

1910   An illustration (XXIX see above) appearing in the Farmer &
        Stockbreeder has the caption – 'A curious breed of sheep on the
        Fitzwilliam Estate, near Peterborough. An unknown breed of
        sheep possessing the ancient name of "Jacob's Flocks", said to be
        descendants of the original sheep tended by Jacob. A pamphlet is at
        present being written on the history of these sheep.'
        Note: Miss Pollard [THE DEANERY] remembered in her youth,
        (born 1899) small round thatched sheep 'huts' specially designed for
        the sheep at Milton.

1913   'Mr George Fitzwilliam has a flock of some 100 breeding ewes;
        nothing is known of their origin, but they probably came from
        WENTWORTH.' See WIGGANTHORPE. HN p. 9.

1964   Listed.

1969   Ram to CALSTONE.

1969   J.S.S. No. 7.

1989   J.S.S. No. 7.

Hungarian Sheep.

XXX.

MONTREAL
Riverhead, Nr. Sevenoaks,
Kent

Field-Marshal The Rt. Hon.
The Lord Amherst K.B., P.C.
b.1717

William Pitt the Elder chose Jeffrey Amherst, then a Major General, to lead the expedition to Canada against the French. Whilst James Wolfe (from nearby Westerham) led an expedition up the St. Lawrence river from the sea to capture Quebec, Amherst led the column that went northward, up the line of the Hudson river, to strike deep into the heart of Canada. He moved an army of nearly 8,000 men to the southern shores of Lake Ontario, embarked his army in whale-boats and country craft and went downstream on the river, moving on Montreal from the west. Here the three armies met up and on 7th. September 1760 the French Commander-in-Chief surrendered himself, his army, and the whole of Canada to General Amherst.

On his return to England and to Riverhead four years later he bought land around the old family home of Brooks in order to create a park. Brooks was pulled down and some of the stones used to build the new house 'Montreal'. In 1794 he had an Obelisk erected to celebrate the happy return of his two brothers and himself, all of whom had fought with distinction in the Army or the Navy; it is engraved with a list of his various victories in North America. It stands in what is now 'Montreal Park Estate' and is all that is left of the house and park shown in this illustration. (Extracts taken from an article by Robin Brooks in 'Bygone Kent' 1980).

By 1778 the house will have been finished and the park occupied by Hungarian Sheep. This was the year that King George III and Queen Charlotte spent the night of 2nd. of November at Montreal before visiting Sevenoaks School and so on to Tunbridge Wells.

It was also the year that Edward Hasted (1732-1812) published his 'History and Topographical Survey of Kent'. In Vol. I page 354 there is an illustration 'Montreal, Seat of Lord Amherst of Holmsdale' by Thomas Sandby (1721-1798) who was pre-eminently an architect; it was his brother Paul who had 'educated in art' the landscape engraver William Watts (1752-1851) who had engraved the picture.

Of great interest are the Hungarian Sheep in the foreground, the only instance that animals are named in the many illustrations contained in the four volumes of 'those noblemen and gentlemen who have so generously and liberally been at the expense of embellishing this work with engravers of their seats.'

XXXI. MONTREAL 1774

Wallachian Sheep

These spotted sheep carry horns identical to those of the Egyptian sheep in Plate I.

Richard Lydekker in his 'Guide to the Domestic Animals...' published in 1908 says on page 23:- 'The Wallachian Sheep as it is commonly known in this country... in Germany as the "Zackelschaf" ' [pronged or pointed sheep] '... appears to have its home in Wallachia and Rumania and some of the adjacent countries of Eastern Europe, the horns, which are of great length, are twisted into close, straight spirals, rising from the head with but little outward divergence. ... In a second breed, apparently a native of Hungary, the horns, although of the same general type, are somewhat more divergent and have the spiral rather more open... Certain horns of the Indian Hunia Ram [Fighting-sheep in India] indicate that there must be a transitional form between the Wallachian and the ordinary Sheep in the matter of horns; for in these Hunia Rams, although the ordinary 'ammon-spiral' is preserved, the horns are extended much more laterally outwards than usual, and at the same time display a more corkscrew-like type of spiral. The intermediate link seems to be formed by a Hungarian breed in which the horns diverge almost directly outwards in a very open spiral, which is however, merely an exaggeration of the ordinary Sheep spiral.'

In H. J. Elwes's 'Guide to the Primitive Breeds of Sheep and their Crosses' published in 1913, he includes an excellent photograph (Fig 42) of the 'Horns of the "Wallachian" or Zacketschaf'. On page 43 he writes:-

'Fig 42 shows the horns of a breed known as "Wallachian," though I can find no evidence of its existance in that country at the present time, though it exists in Hungary. It is a sheep of the same type as the Scotch Black-faced, and has long, coarse wool, and horns of a very remarkable corkscrew shape which usually ascend at various angles, but sometimes, as in the specimen figured, are at right angles to the head. The horns shown measure 38½ inches from tip to tip. A race of sheep with horns of somewhat similar character exists in North-Western China, but nowhere else, as far as I know.'

Note: Lord Amherst's nephew William Pitt Amherst (1805-1886) succeeded to the title and to 'Montreal' in 1797, having been Ambassador to China and Governor-General of India. His grand-daughter, Lady Mary Sarah Amherst married Lord Egerton of TATTON in 1857.

Much Wenlock, Shropshire *T. H. Thursfield*	1910	Flock owner. HN to P.
NANNAU or NEINAU Dolgellau, Gwynedd *Miss Vaughan*	1910	Flock originated from CHARLECOTE. HN to P.
	1913	Listed.
NOBLETHORPE HALL Silkstone, Barnsley, Yorkshire *J. S. H. Fullerton, M.F.H., J.P., D.L., b.1865*	c.1898 -1909	Rams provided from WENTWORTH WOODHOUSE. HN to P.
	c.1904	Ram from WENTWORTH WOODHOUSE. HN p. 10.
	1919	Ram and 6 Ewes presented to Noblethorpe Hall by G. Fitzwilliam of MILTON. HN p. 10.
	1913	40 ewes listed.

NORTH PERROTT Crewkerne, Somerset *Mr. Burton*	1936 -1946	Stock from ALDON.
THE OLD HOUSE Sutton Courtenay, Abingdon, Berkshire *J. F. B. Pomeroy*	1969	J.S.S. No. 43. To daughter, see CALVERLEIGH COURT.
THE OLD HOUSE Withnell Fold, Chorley, Lancashire	1953	Nameless flock owner, author of 1953 list.

THE OLD RECTORY
Lighthorne, Warwick,
Warwickshire

The Hon. Adam Butler
The Rt. Hon. Sir Adam
Butler M.P.

c.1965   3 ewes from Oxhill Manor (Mrs. G. Rodwell) which probably carried CHARLCOTE blood.

1969   J.S.S. No. 86.

1989   J.S.S. No. 86.

OVERBURY COURT
Tewkesbury, Herefordshire

Mr. and Mrs. Thomas Fitz
Gerald. Grandparents of
Admiral FitzGerald of
Shalstone Manor.

Robert M. Holland C.B.,
F.S.A., b.1872

1914   Mr. Heatley Noble writing to Admiral Purefoy:-

'I did not know of Lady Martin's flock and am very pleased to have the particulars you kindly sent.'

1917   Took name of Holland-Martin.

Relationship:- SHALSTONE.

PALACE HOUSE
Beaulieu, Hampshire

Lady Montague of Beaulieu

1970   4 or 5 ewes from CHIDEOCK MANOR.

Ex J.S.S. No. 84.

PARK FARM
Finchingfield, Braintree,
Essex

Mr. Frank Loftus

Had some of his flock from Cambridge University, some from CHATSWORTH.

1949   Sold a British Fresian bull calf to Mrs. Maxwell MAWBIE MAINS, the Luck Pennies were two Jacob lambs.

1964   Gave one year old Jane Baddiley CARLTON FOREST FARM two ewe lambs.

1969   J.S.S. No. 54.

PARK FARM
Hethersett,
Nr. Wymondham, Norfolk

Miss Palmer

c.1948   Sold sheep to Miss Bartholomew of SAHAM – dispersal sale.

PARK PLACE
Henley-on-Thames,
Oxfordshire

Mrs. Noble

1900   Sold Mr. Bradley Firth 30 breeding ewes. HN p. 11.

1909   30 ewes sold to Mr. Diggle. HN p. 11.

1910   Mentioned as flock owner. HN to P.

1913   30 ewes listed. Originated from Henry Micklem [ROSE HILL] who had stock from TABLEY PARK in 1888. HN p. 11.

PETWORTH HOUSE
Petworth, Sussex

George O'Brien, the 3rd.
Earl Egremont

Colonel The Lord Leconfield
b.1787

Quoting from a letter to the author from Historic Buildings Surveyor for Southern Region of the National Trust:-

'the 3rd. Earl experimented with different breeds [of sheep] in the decades either side of 1800. The specific reference is from Dallaway Vol. I p. cxliii (1815). With regard to the deer park he comments:

"Mostly South Downs but also Wiltshire, Somerset and Dorset varieties. These familiar breeds were compared to Leicester,

Hereford, Nottinghamshire and Tiverton varieties as well as more exotic Spanish breeds."

Lord Egremont was advised by Young, one of the authors of the series "A General view of the Agriculture of the County of. . ." '

Note: Arthur Young. 1741-1820.

POLEBROOKE HALL
Nr. Oundel,
Northamptonshire

Colonel A. F. H. Ferguson
b.1867

1904 A ram from WENTWORTH WOODHOUSE, and 6 ewes from MILTON. HN p. 10.

1910 Listed. HN to P.

1913 Flock of 40 ewes

POWERSCOURT HOUSE
County Wicklow, Ireland

Viscount Powerscourt
Bap. 2nd. Nov. 1682

c.1760 George Barret the Elder painted a picture of Powerscourt House with Sugar Loaf Mountain in the background and spotted sheep in the foreground. (See Plate XXV of H. J. Harris's 'The Artist and the Country House 1540-1870.')

Note: Possible relationships with TABLEY, via Ponsonbys, and TONG via Vane Tempests.

POWIS CASTLE
Welshpool, Co. Montgomery,
Wales

The Earl of Powis C.B.E.
b.1889

1971 Sir Hugh Rhys Rankins F.S.A. (Scot.) M.R.I. writing to the author:-

'I write to say that Earl Powis, Welshpool has superb and big boned Jacobs.' in a further letter dated 15th October of same year:- 'Lord Powis used to have superb flock'.

Relationship:- MARLESFORD HALL.

Note: Edward 1st Earl of Powis (1754-1834) was created 'Baron Clive of Walcot in the Co. of Salop' in 1794. The artist James Ward (1769-1859) did some charming sketches (now in private collection) of Indian Cattle in the park of Walcot where there must have been a menagerie. The house is described as 'An 18th century mansion in a great park, acquired by Clive of India (1725-1794) for his retirement.' It would seem more likely that it was Lord Powis who collected rare foreign animals to graze his great park.

POYNTON TOWERS
Highlane, Nr. Stockport,
Cheshire

Rear Admiral Charles
Eustace Anson C.B., M.V.O.
b.1859

1910 'Admiral Anson's flock is being sold'. HN to P.

Relationships:- INGLEBOROUGH, AVISFORD, LULWORTH CASTLE, SCONE, MILTON, STOKE PARK.

PRESTON
Inwardleigh,
Nr. Okehampton, Devon

A. J. Stanbury

c.1959 Writing to the author in 1979:-

'In answer to some of your queries — For over 20 years I've kept upwards of 30 pure Jacob ewes and more, using only pure Jacob rams. I have always had considerable private enquiries for breeding stock, easily selling them all "on the farm", often having more demand than I could supply. I have supplied breeding stock and/or loaned rams for over 50 new flocks. I think my foundation stock came from the Taunton area.

I would be delighted to meet you, and discuss Jacobs further. I am getting on in age and do not travel out of Devon.'

PRESTON LODGE
Withcote, Oakham, Rutland

Sir Henry Tate Bart. M.F.H.
b.1902

1964 Listed.

PRIORS GATE
(The Flat) Priorsfield, Godalming, Surrey

Sir Hugh C. Rhys Rankin F.S.A. (Scot.) Bart., b.1899 Stock Breeder & Sheep Judge

1928 President of the Clun Forest Sheep Breeders Association.

1971 Writing to the author giving list of flock owners.

Of interest are his comments on Jacobs due to the fact that his father had served in South Africa in 1900 and had been Times Correspondent in Morocco in 1908, author of 'With General d'Amade in Morocco'.

Quoting from Sir Hugh's letter:- 'It is interesting that the Indian type of Jacob has the usual "Eastern ears" i.e. floppy and hanging down – to avoid the dust. And that these ears have changed in course of being in Europe. (Much is said even in Mesta events in old Spain, of "speckled sheep" kept amongst the Mesta Merino) See J. Klein "The Mesta" 1920.'

In another letter of same year:- 'I think Jacobs are the original sheep which spread all over Europe from Sumeria and Syria. i.e. Desert sheep NOT mountain sheep and that perhaps, the spots were original natural colouring of all DESERT sheep. Alternatively, are they the only breed which does not descend from Urial and Moufflon etc.?'

PYLEWELL PARK
Lymington, Hampshire

Mr. W. Ingham Whitaker b.1866

1909 Purchase flock from Mr. Heatley Noble. HN p. 11.

1910 Listed. HN to P.

RAGLINGTON FARM
Shedfield, Southampton, Hampshire

R. Kendal Ockenden

1964 Listed.

RAINWORTH
Nr. Mansfield, Nottinghamshire

J. Whitaker

* Author of "Discriptive List of the Deer Parks & Paddocks of England".

1892 From Mr. Lowndes' [CASTLE COMBE] sheep book 'The sheep given me by Lady Cowley were the foundation of my "Zulu" flock; the ram given by Mr. Whittaker. . . were all black or nearly so, with only the face, tail and a leg or two white, and they never had more than two horns. . . they were crossed with piebald sheep from Mr. Whitaker. . .' HN 14 and 15.

1894 Presented stock to the Duke of Portland [WELBECK ABBEY]. HN p. 14.

1905 Obtained stock from Sir Charles Tempest [BROUGHTON HALL]. HN p. 14.

1905 Sold some to Mr. William Hollins [BURSLEM]. HN p. 14.

1908 Listed by R. Lydekker in his 'Guide to the Domesticated Animals' p. 21.

1913 10 ewes sold to Mr. J. P. Chaworth-Musters [ANNERSLEY]. HN p. 14.

In an undated letter headed 'Tuesday' to Colonel Platt, Mr. Whitaker writes:-

'I take the greatest interest in animals especially what I call the spotted four horned sheep Spanish Sheep & I feel sure the time when they were first introduced was when the Armada lost so many vessels on our western islands' [See Tabley]. . . . 'There is a very pretty picture of mine in 'Scribblings of a Hedgerow Naturalist' W. Black, Publisher, Sherwood Street. . . price 5/- post paid. (Author has been unable to find.*)

There then follow drawings of various horn formations.

The coat is of a heavy nature but soft and woolly next to the skin, this seems to throw back to a pure wild breed sometime.'

* Published 1898 by Ballantyne, Hanson & Co.

RAVENDALE FARM
Higham Gobion, Hitchin,
Hertfordshire
Mr. and Mrs. J. H. Latimer

1955	Two shearling Ewes from KING'S WALDEN. A ram from SHALSTONE.
1969	J.S.S. No. 16.
1989	J.S.S. No. 16.

REDENHAM PARK
Andover, Hampshire
A. Kidstone
Mrs. N. M. D. Sheffield

Pre 1968	Original flock from various sources.
1968	J.S.S. No. 92.
1989	J.S.S. No. 92. See SUTTON PARK.

ROCKCLIFFE PARK
Darlington, Yorkshire
R. Swan

c.1905	25 breeding ewes, presented by Mr. George Fitzwilliam. [MILTON]. HN p. 10.
1910	Listed. HN to P.
1913	Possesses 25 breeding ewes. HN p. 10.

ROSEHILL
Henley-on-Thames,
Oxfordshire
Major General Edward Micklem, b. c.1842
Lt. Colonel Henry A. Micklem D.S.O., b.1872

1879	Had sheep from Dryden [CANON'S ASHBY]. HN p. 11.
1888	Heatley Noble had 60 ewes from Henry Micklem – who had them from TABLEY. HN p. 11.

RYCOTE PARK
(Ricot) Thame, Oxfordshire
Rt. Hon. the Lord Norreys (Norris) b.1579

Tab. 10 Fig. 10

Tab. 10 Fig. 11

XXXII. Rycote Park 1677

1677 Robert Plot (1640-1696) in his 'Natural History of Oxfordshire' mentions on page 188 No. 39. 'But there are much stranger sheep though perhaps not so profitable, at Ricot in the Park of the Right Honourable the Lord Norreys, brought hither from some other parts of England or Wales, but now breeding here: Of which, some of them at first had six or eight horns apiece, but the number upon mixture of their generation with other sheep is since diminish'd. However, there remain still two of them with very strange heads, having each four horns; one of them with two larger ones issuing from the top of its head, bending forward, and two side ones coming out from under its ears, and bending round towards its mouth, as in Tab. 10. Fig. 10. And the other having two large horns standing pretty upright on its head, and two side ones proceeding from under the ears like the former, and bending round to the cheeks, into which they would grow (and so in the whole kind) were they not prevented by being timely cut off, as in Tab. 10. Fig. 11.'

Unfortunately Mr. Plot does not mention the colour of the fleece; his works were 'marked by great credulity'. In 1683 he was appointed first 'Custos' of the Ashmolean Museum in Oxford.

The Norreys family inherited the property in the 16th century. The great house burnt down in 1745 and its remains demolished in 1800 except for one corner turret and some outbuildings. These still stand, the former stables converted into the present house by Winstanley c.1920. The lake was created by Lancelot (Capability) Brown about 1770.

Sir Henry, 1st Baron Norris of Rycote (1525?-1601) was shown exceptional favour by Queen Elizabeth, whom he entertained at Rycote in 1566 and 1592. His son, Sir John (1547?-1597) assisted in preparations to resist the Armade. . . took command with Drake of the expedition to the coast of Spain 1589 and 1593. Returned to Ireland in 1595 where he died at Mallow, Munster. Francis, Earl of

Berkshire K.B. (1579-1623) grandson of Sir Henry was 'in attendance on the Earl of Nottingham in Spain in 1605; he was imprisoned in the Fleet Gaol in consequence of an encounter with Lord Scrope in the House of Lords in 1621, and 'shot himself with a cross-bow from mortification.'

It was James Bertie, 5th Lord Norris (who became the 1st Earl of Abingdon) who must have had these curious sheep in his Park; he was baptised in 1653 and died in 1699 having been created Baron Norreys of Rycote in 1675, two years before Mr. Plot's book was published.

ROUSHAM **Steeple Aston, Oxfordshire** *Mr. Cottrell-Dormer, b. c.1897*	1940 -1950	Had sheep from SHALSTONE.

SAHAM
Saham Toney,
Swaffham, Norfolk

Miss Hermione Bartholomew

c.1949 Had flock from Miss Palmer of PARK FARM, Hethersett, Nr. Norwich, her grandfather's flock having been sold the year before. (See BLAKESLEY HALL) having become cross-bred.

1964 Listed.

1969 Founder member J.S.S. No. 3.

SCALFORD HALL
(BURTON HILL)
Melton Mowbray,
Leicestershire

Mrs. F. D. G. Colman
b. c. 1888

c.1953 Had sheep from KING'S WALDEN.

-70 Had sheep from CLOUGH HOUSE FARM and a ram from SAHAM. Writing to the author in 1973, Miss Bartholomew describes them 'They were a real good flock not touched for 50 years and are *Jacob Sheep*, no nonsense of crossing in, and out, kept pure at Scalford, a lot of them not pretty, I have a number and they are wild and spindly (not your fancy) but they are the longstanding Jacob breed'.

1969 J.S.S. No. 34 with 55 sheep.

c.1972 Flock to her neice, Lady Wendy Lycett, of West Grange, Scots Gap. Now J.S.S. No. 34.

1989 J.S.S. No. 34.

SCONE PALACE
Perth, Scotland

The Earl of Mansfield M.P.
b.1900

Director of Highland and Agricultural Society of Scotland 1929-32. President of the Perthshire Agricultural Society and of Scottish Chamber of Agriculture 1936-37. Governor of Edinburgh and East of Scotland College of Agriculture 1925-30.

The Earl of Mansfield and Mansfield, D.L., J.P. Ordinary Director of Royal Highland and Agricultural Society 1976-79. First Crown Estate Commissioner 1985.

Letter from Lady Mansfield and Mansfield to the author in 1988.

c.1930 'One of our retired farm managers [Mr Black] has told me that
-40 as far as he can recall the original sheep did not actually come from Abercairney. The story is that the late Earl was shooting with Mr. Drummond-Moray and indicated that he would like a few of the "spotted" sheep to graze around the Palace. Mr. Drummond-Moray had then said that he would have to get them from him because he had the only flock at the time. The Earl made a bet of £5 that he could get them elsewhere.

At the time he was a Director of Whipsnade Zoo and knew that they had some of the Jacob Sheep. He also knew that they wanted a Highland Bull so he swapped the Bull for a tup and 4 females thus winning his bet.

I have not been able to find out exactly when this happened but as far as Mr. Black's memory could remember it was the late 1930s early 1940s.'

1963 Listed.

1970 Lord Mansfield writing to the author:-

'I see no reason why the picture of our ram should not be made into a Christmas Card, as it appears to me to be entirely suitable for reproduction. . . .It sounds excellent that a thesis is to be written on the breed; only I hope it wont be done too soon as there is bound to be a lot of information appearing from unexpected sources, when the project becomes known.' (See p. 28 XIX)

1969 J.S.S. No. 52.

1971 'We have had wonderful lambing this year, with several sets of triplets and the rams are all of really good quality.' Lord Mansfield to author.

1989 J.S.S. No. 52.
Relationship:- ABERCAIRNEY.

XXXIII. SCOTLAND LODGE 1964

SCOTLAND LODGE
Winterbourne Stoke,
Salisbury, Wiltshire

Mr. R. Wales, b. c.1905

1964 Photographed with his flock of Jacobs. Mr. Wales, a Northumbrian, had come down to farm on Salisbury Plain. A true conservationist of rare breeds, a breeder of British White and Longhorn Cattle.

Writing to the author in 1968 – in beautiful copper-plate handwriting – he inferred that many people had tried to set up a society for Jacob sheep, all had failed, it was an impossible task; but wished her the best of luck.

1966 6 Ewes from CALSTONE for service, only 5 returned due to over active ram.

1969 J.S.S. No. 33.

SHALSTONE MANOR
Shalstone, Buckingham,
Buckinghamshire

Admiral Richard Purefoy
Fitzgerald RN., C.B.E.,
M.V.C., b.1862
Assumed name of Purefoy
1899

Geoffrey P. Purefoy

Simon H. L. Purefoy

c.1914 Handwritten note by R. P. in his copy of Mr. Heatley Noble's 'An Effort to Trace The History and the so-called "Spanish" Piebald Sheep' on page 12, says:-

1850 'The Shalstone Flock originally came from Sir H. Dryden at CANON'S ASHBY sometime about 1850 I believe.'

1914 Mr. Heatley Noble writing to the Admiral.

'Dear Sir, I shall be very pleased to have a two horned ram lamb from you next Spring. Personally I do not use two horned rams, but even now, after more than 25 years breeding from none but four horned animals not more than 25% of the male lambs come with four, and I generally sell a great number of them. The lambs are weaned in August and I will write to you again later. I have no yearling rams with two horns as I find there is little sale for them but I have half a dozen with 4.'

1881 Sir Henry Dryden writes to Captain Fitz Gerald at his house North Hall, Basingstoke [Preston Candover] though the sheep were always at Shalstone. 'Dear Fitz-Gerald, I am very sorry to learn that you have been so unfortunate as to be under surgeons and can only hope you will not again need such an unpleasant assistance. I send a few views about the sheep. If you have any to part with I have a customer. Mr. A. Reynell Pack of Avisford, Nr. Arundel, whose mother was a Miss Hutchinson, has a few of the breed, originally from mine, and has written to me to ask to buy more. I don't want to sell any but must supply him if you can't. I hope that, as you had some not long ago to part with, you can supply him with some ewes. Let me know directly. I hope Mrs. F.G. and your youngsters are well. Remember me to her. Yours truly H. Dryden.'

1934 Stock from TABLEY.

1940 Sheep to ROUSHAM.
-50

1964 Listed.

1969 J.S.S. No. 9.

1970 Ram to CALSTONE.

1989 J.S.S. Nos. 8 & 9.

Relationship:- OVERBURY.

Note 1: This flock has probably the longest direct blood line. Miss Jervoise born 1809 had Pied Sheep by the time she married Mr. Thomas FitzGerald, to become grandparents of the Admiral. He in turn has a great grandson who is J.S.S. Member No. 8.

Note 2: The present owner of the flock, tells the story that the sheep which came from Canon's Ashby c.1840 were in payment of a debt owed to Admiral Purefoy which was settled with Jacob Sheep.

SHANBALLY CASTLE 1932

XXXVII

XXXV

SHANBALLY CASTLE
Clogheen, Tipperary, Ireland

The Lady Constance Butler
b.1879

1910 Lady Constance Butler has 6 breeding ewes at Kilkenny Castle (her home). HN to P.

Her nephew, Sir John Carew Pole wrote to the author in 1984. 'My aunt's name was Lady Constance Butler, Shanbally Castle, Clogheen, Co. Tipperary which belonged to her and my mother jointly and she kept the flock there. To the best of my memory they were there before the first war and in the 1920s and we all were given tweed made from their wool – long since worn out. . . Sadly Shanbally was sold after the 2nd World War and pulled down.'

Her niece, Miss Marye Pole-Carew writing the same year says:- 'I have no knowledge or memory of when my Aunt first started collecting her flock of Jacobs or from where she obtained them – certainly a long while ago – about the beginning of the century!'

3rd July 1984 'At last I have found an old photograph album of my Aunt's and see that she dated the same duplicate photos (that I sent you) as 1932 – so presume she kept the flock anyway up till the Second World War. My aunt's sheep were known as "Jacob's" flock and neither Algerian or Barbary sheep!'

J.S.S. No. 898.

Relationships:- WIGGANTHORPE,
WENTWORTH WOODHOUSE.

XXXVI

SHAWDON HALL
Glanton, Alnwick,
Northumberland

Major C. Bewicke

1963 Listed.

SISSINGHURST CASTLE
Cranbrook, Kent

The Hon. Vita Sackville West
F.R.S.L. (The Hon. Mrs.
Harold Nicholson) b.1892

N. Nicolson

1939   Flock established; see article published in 'Country Notes' entitled 'Jacob's Sheep' – part of which is quoted on page 22.

1963   Listed.

SKENE HOUSE
Skene, Nr. Aberdeen, Aberdeenshire, Scotland

Brigadier-General J. G. H.
Hamilton D.S.O., b.1869

c.1900   Was given a gift of Jacob sheep.
The flock went to his nephew at Lullenden, East Grinstead.
So to his daughter J.S.S. No. 63 [WHITEHOPE].
Relationship:- LOWOOD.

SMALLBURGH HILL
Smallburgh, Norwich, Norfolk

C. R. Pollit

1964   Listed

SOMERFORD PARK
Somerford cum Radnor

Sir Walter G. Shakerley Bt.
b.1859

1910   Listed. HN to P.

1913   'Sir Walter Shakerley has a flock of 50 to 60 ewes. Origin quite unknown. Said to have been in the Park as long as the wild cattle, i.e. 200 years.' HN p. 10.

1913   In H. J. Elwes's 'Guide. . .' p. 34 'Fig 24 is an old four-horned ram bred at Somerford Park.' The illustration on p. 59 shows rather a white Jacob, with black feet and knees; a good head with badger face and four good horns.
Note 1: The Archivist at the Cheshire Record Office writes in 1989 as follows:
'The Oldfields held the manor there from Elizabethan times to 1701 when the Shakerleys acquired it. . . [i.e. c.200 years earlier.]
The Shakerley MSS are now deposited here but will not be available for study for a while yet.'
Note 2: Peter Shakerley, who died in 1558, had married Elizabeth Mainwaring of Over Peover the village of nearby TABLEY.
Relationships:- COLDHAYES, HAMMERWOOD, THE CLIFF.

SOUTH WEALD PARK
Brentwood, Essex

Charles J. H. Turner

Listed by SH.

STAINBOROUGH HALL
Barnsley, South Yorkshire

Captain Bruce Wentworth
b.1862
(Captain Bruce Canning
Vernon Wentworth J.P., M.P.
later of WENTWORTH
CASTLE)

1909   Mr. Wigfield the Agent at WOODHOUSE WENTWORTH writing to Colonel Platt includes 'Stainbro' Hall' in a list of estates to which he has sent Rams since 1898.
Note: The Archivist of the Sheffield City Libraries, writing in 1989:-
'The Vernon-Wentworth Manuscripts (Wentworth Castle) estate records refer predominantly to industrial matters rather than agricultural, but a farm account book of 1912-1921 (VWM 169) records transactions relating to Jacob sheep.' Alas this has not been followed up.

1913   Listed. 'Captain Bruce Vernon-Wentworth owns a flock of twenty ewes. There is no authentic information as to their origin, but they are said to have been imported by the Earl of Strafford in 1730.' HN p. 15.
Note: The 1st Earl of Strafford was born in 1772 and could have 'imported' them from Ireland or Spain.

STOKE PARK **Towcester,** **Northamptonshire** *Mr. Vernon*	Pre 1840 Writing in 1881, Sir Henry Dryden says:- 'I believe that in 1840 Mr. Vernon of STOKE PARK near Towcester had the breed.'
STOWFORD MANOR **FARM** **Wingfield, Trowbridge,** **Wiltshire** *G. A. Bryant*	1964 Listed.
STUDLEY ROYAL **Ripon, North Yorkshire** *Mr. John Aislabie 1670-1742* *Mr. William Aislabie d.1781*	1799 -1802 'There has been a breed of mottled sheep (brought originally from Spain) kept at Aislabie park (I think) in Yorkshire for nearly half a century past, which still retain all their distinct peculiarities, if I be rightly informed, as pure as when first brought over. The wool of these sheep was in Spain of a very coarse quality, and of little value, as it is at this day in Britain. . .' From:- James Anderson Ll.D. 'Recreations in Agriculture, Natural-History, Arts and Miscellaneous Literature. 1799-1802 Vol. II p. 174.

STUDLEY ROYAL (continued):

1834   James Bell's Gazetteer lists two locations in Yorkshire named Aislaby, one in the parish of Whitby, the second near Pickering 'partly in the parish of Middleton'.

It has been suggested that James Anderson's entry could have been 'Mr. Aislabie's park' as no Aislaby Park has been discovered.

The Deer Park at Studley Royal had been well established by John Aislabie's mother's family when he inherited it in 1699. On the death of William Aislabie the estate passed to his daughter and then to her neice, both of whom rarely visited Studley. The garden and park were subsequently preserved by later members of the Vyner family, descendants of the Aislabies, until both were purchased by West Riding County Council in 1966. The National Trust acquired the estate in 1983 and has embarked on a major scheme of restoration and conservation to restore Studley to its former glory.

Note: No evidence has been found that there were sheep of any kind in the Park either from pictures or estate documents; unfortunately many records were burnt in a fire some years ago.

Note: See AISLABIE PARK.

SUDBURY HALL **Sudbury, Nr. Derby,** **Derbyshire** *The Lord Vernon D.L., b.1889*	His father, born 1854, was a member of the royal commission on agriculture 1893-4. Listed SH. Relationship:- LYVEDEN.
SUDDENE PARK FARM **Burbage, Marlborough,** **Wiltshire** *G. Gent*	1964 Listed. c.1965 Sold Colonel and Mrs. Peter Luard [CALSTONE] 6 ewes.
Sutton Scarsdale, **Chesterfield, Derbyshire** *Mr. Clarke*	1762 '6 mottled sheep from Mr. Clarke of Sutton Scarsdale for £3. 2s. 0d.' Paid to John Bacon, probably a tenant. Ref. Folio 205v CHATSWORTH.
SUTTON PARK **Sutton-on-the-Forest, York,** **North Yorkshire** *Mrs. N. M. D. Sheffield*	c.1975 Had her son's flock from REDENHAM. 1989 J.S.S. No. 92.

XXXVIII. TABLEY PARK The Old Hall 1760

TABLEY HOUSE
Knutsford, Cheshire

Old Tabley House

De Tabley Park

Sir John Fleming Leicester
Baron de Tabley, b.1762

1730　In a letter dated 30th October 1934, Charles Byrne Leicester-Warren (b.1896) writing to Mr. Heatley Nobles says:-

'In reply to your letter concerning the spotted sheep, this flock has been here since 1730, having been brought over from Ireland by Sir John Byrne who married the Leicester heiress. They really are Persian, but I believe the Syrians are much the same. My flock has the Armada legend, hence the misnomer "Spanish".

I change rams with 4 or 5 places where the flocks are more or less pure, the last one being from Drummond-Moray of Abercairny.

They are four-horned, two sometimes curly. They are very hardy, and the mutton is excellent.'

Charles Warren, as he was then known, had served in Iraq and Persia in 1820.

1784　In a letter from Sir Henry Dryden dated 1884, (presumably to Mr. Heatley Noble) he says:-

'The breed has been at Tabley for nearly 200 years, as is shown by an old painting of the house at a certain date. Lord De Tabley has, I think, no special name for them except "Spotted". The Tabley rams had straight horns, nearly all had four, and very long; but when he had a ram from me many came with the twisted horns, and Lord De Tabley complained that I had spoilt the beauty of his flock. At Tabley they kept all the hes [sic] as rams for ornament, and never ate any of the mutton. These gentry were let to live as long as they could, and amused themselves by continual fighting. . . The size of the Tabley horns had much decreased from, I suppose, breeding in and in.'

As so much of the 'evidence' used by various authors has referred to the '1760 Tabley picture', a black and white photograph of the original oil painting by Anthony T. Devis (1729-1817) is here reproduced. As can be seen the sheep are white, two carrying horns. (XXXVIII see above.

Writing in 1989 from the Estate Office, the present Land Agent says:-

'This is one of a set of five paintings of the park at Tabley by Anthony Devis in the late 1760's – just after the new house was built. Four of the paintings depict some sheep but none, as can be seen from the example enclosed, could be described as spotted or skewbald – they are all white. On very close examination it seems that some of them do have two pairs of horns. Most of the family papers are now in the County Records Office at Chester but I... do not know of any references to the sheep... they are very extensive... have not been closely studied from this point of view.

He adds:-

'Incidently he [Sir Francis Leicester] also commissioned a painting of the new house and park by Richard Wilson.'

Note: This has not been researched.

Bryan's Dictionary of Painters and Engravers' (1914) lists a painting by James Ward (1769-1859) of 'De Tabley Park' as being held by Oldham Art Gallery, Manchester, alas this painting is not listed in their present collection.

1826 Important Note:-

On July 10th 1826 Sir John Fleming Leicester, Bart. was 'elevated to the peerage as Baron de Tabley of Tabley House'. As he was 'distinguished as a munificient patron of fine arts, and supporter of native artists' surely it is possible that he commissioned James Ward, that same year, to paint the sheep in his park. 'He died deeply lamented 18th June 1827' See page 96, and Plate XLV p. 97. It still has to be established that there was a ruined church tower standing at the time.

The two lithographs of 'Persian Sheep' drawn by Sir Francis Leicester in 1822 carry two straight horns and two lower curled horns; the straight horns do not appear in the painting of four years later. By 1934 Mr. Charles Leicester-Warren maintains that his flock 'are four-horned, two straight, and two sometimes curley' (see Plate XL of photographs of about this date). The introduction of Sir Henry Dryden's one ram in 1879 and in subsequent years which 'spoilt the beauty of his flock' could hardly have stamped the whole flock at once; they could have reproduced some of the genes of the original sheep as painted by Ward.

Writing in 1881, Sir Henry Dryden says:-

'Lord De Tabley's rams had usually 4 straight horns till he crossed with mine after which many had curled horns. Ours have almost always curled horns.' (Northamptonshire Record Office Ref. D (CA) 500)

Amongst the Dryden papers is one headed:-

'Visit to Tabley April 16th 1909.

Spanish Sheep, called by them Persian.

Rams all 4 horns, shape very mixed.

Ewes two horns a very few with four.

Nearly all black & white.

Marked in large blotches.

A very few brown & white in spots.

Flock uneven in type.'

XXXIX. Sketches 'of Ram's Heads of the Persian Breed', Tabley 1822.

Pre Mr. Henry Micklam [ROSE HILL] had them from Tabley.
1888 HN p. 11.

(These then went on to Mr. Heatley Noble as a flock of 60 ewes, and so to TEMPLE COMBE and PARK PLACE.)

1913 Mr. Heatley Noble in his article, page 10 says:-

'Lady Leighton-Warren [TABLEY] owns a flock of 26 breeding ewes. This is undoubtedly one of the oldest known. It is from here that the Armada story has been handed down, ...it is certain the pied sheep have been at Tabley since about 1760 as shown by a picture painted at that date, and there seems no reason why they may not have roamed the park many years before. Writing in

XL. Sheep in Park c.1934

August 1910, Mr. Richmond gives me the following interesting particulars of this flock. "I was agent from 1879 to 1887 to George Warren, Lord De Tabley. When I went there I found a worn-out flock of the black and white sheep wandering about the Park. During the first autumn I persuaded the owner to buy a ram from the late Sir Henry Dryden. . . and for many years we annually exchanged rams. During this time a ram was purchased from CHATSWORTH flock, so that we really did save the Tabley flock from extinction.'

Pre 1934 Mr. C. Leicester-Warren writing to Mr. Heatley Noble:-
(See 1730 entry – repeated.)

'I change rams with 4 or 5 places where the flocks are more or less pure, the last being from Drummond-Moray of ABERCAIRNY.'

1934 Stock to SHALSTONE.

Note: Re. Persian Sheep.

In A. R. Werner's publication of c.1975 'An Enquiry into the Origin of the Piebald or "Jacob" Sheep p. 75 he states:- 'The only physical characteristic that had been taken seriously recently, is a defect in the upper eyelid that had previously been recorded only in Karakul sheep. If the two breeds did have a comparatively recent, common ancestor, as Littlejohn (1969) has suggested, the link with Piebald sheep is through the Danadar indigenous to Western Turkestan, Western Persia and Afghanistan until their extinction about 1843. One lithograph of a four-horned, Piebald ram labelled 'of the Persian breed' (TABLEY) is the only traditional evidence that links the breed with this part of Asia, and it is yet to be established, if indeed it ever can be, whether the defect demonstrates a genuine affinity between the extinct Danadar and Piebald sheep.'

(A. I. Littlejohn 1969 'The Veterinary Record' Vol. 85, No. 7).

The Armada Story.

At the end of the last century in 'Live Stock Handbooks No. 1. Sheep, Breeds & Management' page 91:-

'Herdwick Sheep. The story goes that "forty small sheep managed to save themselves from the wreck of one of those Spanish galleons," . . .on the sandy Cumberland shore at Drigg these forty sheep saved themselves and "were claimed as jetsam and flotsam by the lord of the manor" '.

To try to substantiate this legend, of how, in 1588 pied sheep jumped ashore from the ships driven onto the Cumberland coast is nearly impossible but there is perhaps a clue, where Jacob sheep are concerned, in the fact, that the Ponsonby (Bessborough) family take their name from the lordship of Ponsonby, a village only two miles from the coast, just north of Sellafield. Drigg is some seven miles south of Ponsonby.

In 1605 Henry Ponsonby marries, of his two sons Sir John and Henry, the eldest married secondly Elizabeth widow of Richard Wingfield of Powerscourt [POWERSCOURT], he was Sheriff of Co. Wicklow and Kilkenny in 1654. He left a considerable fortune when he died in 1668 when his Irish Estates were inherited by Sir Henry Ponsonby of Bessborough, Co. Kilkenny, Elizabeth's eldest son. Sir John's brother Henry went to Ireland in 1649 and married Rose Weldon of Raheen, Queen's County.

The link may lie in the fact that Daniel Byrne, or O'Byrne author of 'A History of the Queen's County', published in Dublin 1856 dedicated his book to 'Right Hon. Lord de Tabley: Castle of Timogue'.

Reproduced is Plate XLIX p. 99 a map of Queens County by J.S.S. No. 581 (an Honours History Graduate of Trinity College, Dublin), who says:-

'I have found this lovely 6″ to mile Townland Survey in the library at Portlaios (the old Maryborough). It covers the county in 36 huge sheets, each signed and dated by the surveyor in August and September 1841. Timogue, Rathin House [Ratheen], Kilmoroney House, and Ballynakill are on sheets 19, 25, 26 & 30. . . I can guarantee that they are in the right places. Rathin and Kilmoroney look as if they are out on a limb but in fact there are bridges over the Barrow and the Grand Canal to the main Athy-Carlow road in the next county, in sight of the house.

For nineteen years we find the lands in possession of the crown, that is from their forteiture in 1641, to the period of the grant to Robert Fitzgerald in 1660; on his recovering the lands he sold those of Timogue, Ballyleskin, Lugacurran and twelve other townlands to Daniel O'Byrne, father of Sir Gregory O'Byrne for £120,000.'

Daniel Byrne, who's properties were Slane and Timogue in Queen's Co., was buried on 24th January 1683; he was the Great Grandfather of Sir John Byrne Bart. who married the 'Leicester Heiress' mentioned by Mr. Charles Leicester-Warren in his letter to Mr. Heatley Noble. She was Meriel, only daughter of Sir Francis Leicester Bart. from 'a family of very great antiquity in the county of Cheshire, the house, 'Old' Tabley Hall having been built by John Leycester (sic) in 1373. (Tabley House, half a mile away was not built until 1760). Sir Francis's grandfather had been a celebrated antiquarian and historian and been created 1st Baronet in 1660, but as Sir Francis had no son this line became extinct. In 1704 Anna Warren of Poynton, Cheshire married Sir Daniel Byrne and it was their son who married Meriel Leicester in 1728. By his Will, Sir Francis stipulated that his only daughter Meriel's son, Sir Peter Byrne (who built the house in 1760) should take the name of

Leicester; also that he was to sell his Irish Estates and use the proceeds to buy further lands in Cheshire.

The Estate Agent of Tabley House (now the property of Victoria University of Manchester) says in a letter of 1989 to the author:-

'It seems most likely that the sheep were brought over by Sir Peter when he moved to Cheshire having sold his Irish Estates.'

In 1988 Colin Martin & Geoffrey Parker's 'The Spanish Armada' was published. On page 245 they state:-

'So far as is known, the coast of England reaped only a single wreck. She was the hospital ship "San Pedro Mayor", a 580-ton hulk which, after rounding the British Isles, fetched up on Bolt Tail in Devon on 6th November'.

The authors also mention that the ships 'were not designed for long periods at sea, or for extended voyages, and so the problems of victualling were minimal. . . Virtually the full capacity of the ship was given over to weapons and men, who were expected to remain on board only long enough for a foray across the Channel.' They state, 'this mass of documentary evidence. . . has allowed us, in effect, actually to go on board the ships themselves and examine their contents as they were in 1588.'

In their Introduction they say:-

'In the terrible aftermath of the Armada more than thirty Spanish ships were lost off the western coasts of Scotland and Ireland.' Extracts from the publisher's notes tell of the 'huge quantity of previously unstudied material in the great archives of Spain and the Netherlands. . . the two authors have put together the pieces of the puzzle in a way never before possible. The Spanish Armada is at last fully explained, and some unexpected conclusions reached. In the process several long-established myths are laid to rest.'

It is possible that the Ponsonby family took the 'Persian' sheep to Ireland when land settlements were being made in 1556 when Queen's Co. was created. Sir John had two grants of lands under the Acts of Settlement. Perhaps during the next thirty years the Byrne family nearby obtained some of these sheep – the progeny of which were taken back to Cheshire by Sir John when he married Meriel Leicester of Tabley in 1728. The link may lie in the Weldon family of Kilmoroney, only given up by the family in 1947; this family had lived at Rathin House before Kilmoroney was built.

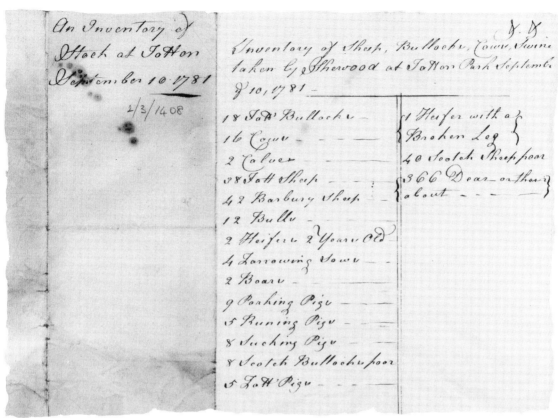

XLI. TATTON PARK 1781

TATTON PARK
Knutsford, Cheshire

William Tatton Egerton, M.P.
b.1749

1781   John Sherwood to William Egerton.
'Inventory of Sheep, Bullocks, Cows, Swine taken by Sherwood at Tatton Park, September 10, 1781. . .
42 Barbury (sic) Sheep.'
Ref John Rylands University Library of Manchester. Egerton of Tatton 2/3/1408 233/89. Plate XLI see above.

1910   Mr. Heatley Noble writing to Colonel Platt mentions:-
'Lord Egerton of Tatton's flock are black sheep – St Kilda?'

1915   At the GRANGE PARK sale Lady Egerton of Tatton bought a Ram lamb for £2. 11. 0.

TEMPLE COMBE
Henley-on-Thames,
Oxfordshire

Mr. Heatley Noble

1888   Origin of flock from Mr. Henry Micklem [ROSE HILL] who had them from TABLEY. HN p. 11.

Pre 1909   Had a ram from AVISFORD – Dryden blood. Ref HN to P.

1909   Asking Colonel Platt [GORDDINOG] for ram.
27th March. Article in The Field 'The African Pied Four-Horned Sheep' by Heatley Noble.

1913   Published 'An Effort to Trace the History of the so-called "Spanish" Piebald Sheep'.

1915   Flock of 60. HN p. 11.

1914   Ordering a two-horned ram from Admiral Purefoy [SHALSTONE] for next season.

Note: Without the endless research done by Mr. Heatley Noble, at the suggestion of Colonel Henry Platt, the various blood lines which have been traced in this book could not have been recorded.

THORESBY PARK
Newark, Nottinghamshire

The Earl Manvers, b.1737

Pre 1767 In 2nd August 1979 'Correspondence' of Country Life a letter, together with an illustration, was published entitled 'Touching Homage'. The caption to the illustration reads '18th-century amateur watercolour of Thoresby Hall, Nottinghamshire.' This letter, from Clive Aslet states that it is a view of the mansion that Carr of York built in 1767-71. The urn, still standing in 1989, has an inscription which reads 'To the Memory of Evelyn Pierrepont, Second Duke of Kingston . . . a touching homage to the builder of the house.' He had left his estates to his nephew Charles Medows (sic) who took the name of Pierrepont in 1788, to became Baron Pierrepont of HOLME PIERREPOINT in 1796, and Earl Manvers in 1806.

In the watercolour fourteen animals are depicted of which eight are dark Jacob sheep, only one of which is truly pied carrying four horns; the rest of the animals might be cows, one may be a black pig.

In 1661 Sir Philip Meadows married Constance, daughter and co-heiress of Francis Lucy, youngest brother of Sir Francis Lucy of CHARLCOTE, which is perhaps where these sheep originated.

THORPE MANDERVILLE
Middleton Cheney, Northamptonshire

Mrs. Lush

Sir Henry Dryden writing to Captain FitzGerald [SHALSTONE] in 1881 mentions 'Mrs. Lush'. He says:-

c.1884
c.1874 'I had the beginning of my flock from Col. Hutchinson of WESTON near this place about 40 years ago. He had the breed from a lady at Thorpe Manderville several years before that.'

On page 11 of Mr. Heatley Noble's article he quotes Sir Henry Dryden [CANON'S ASHBY] as saying in a letter dated 1897:-

c.1839 -40
c.1800 'Mine came from Col. Hon. H. Hely Hutchinson about 1839 or 1840. He had them from Thorpe Manderville where the breed had been for many years, probably about 1800.'

Note: Sir Henry was born 1818.

TICHBORNE PARK
Alresford, Hampshire

Sir Henry Tichborne D.L.
b.1866

Pre 1910 Listed by Heatley Noble writing to Colonel Platt as 'the late Sir H. Tichborne'.

Also listed by SH.

TONG HALL
Drighlington, Nr. Bradford, West Yorkshire

Sir Tristram Tempest Bart.
b.1865

1909 Sir Tristram died in June, there is a letter dated October 1909 from the Estate Manager at Wentworth Woodhouse giving a list of those people he has supplied with rams since 1898 which mention Sir Tristram, without the words 'the late'.

1922 A letter from the Estate Office (Nigel Finch Hatton) enquiring from another Estate Land Agent at Northampton:-

'I wrote to you in September 1920 with reference to a Spanish Ram. If you have a good Shearling Spanish Ram to dispose of with four horns, I could exchange one with you. Our flock are pure bred and well marked, and we have had Rams from the Duke of Devonshire, Earl Fitzwilliam, and Sir John Barker's flocks.

The Ram I could exchange has four horns, and am sure would give satisfaction. The Ram is a Shearling.'

This letter will have been to MILTON; Earl Fitzwilliam being at Wentworth Woodhouse at that date.

1924 A letter from the Estate Office as above to Sir Arthur Dryden [CANON'S ASHBY]:-

'I am requiring a Four horned Shearling Ram. . . which I shall be prepared to purchase for cash, or exchange for a two year old Ram. The Ram I could exchange would I think give satisfaction, it came from the Duke of Devonshire's flock.'

Snowdonia

1913 'There is a flock at Tong Hall, origin unknown, but said to have been there since the time of the Armada. About thirty-five ewes kept for breeding'. HN p. 14.

(Tells of a TABLEY connection perhaps?)

Listed SH.

Writing to the author in 1989, the Clerical Officer of Bradford District Archives says:-

'I have checked the farming records in the Tong Hall collections, but have not found anything connected with different breeds of sheep. I have also checked various other sources in our Archives, but to no avail.'

Note: The Archives of North Yorkshire County Record Office have not as yet been checked.

Possible relationships:- BILTON, TICHBORNE.

VAYNOL PARK
Port Dinorwic, Caernarvon, North Wales

Sir Robert G. V. Duff Bart. b.1876

Listed by SH.

The Estate Agent of c.1950 (Viscount Stuart of Finhorn) confirms that there was a Menagerie or Wild Park of curious animals including Wild White cattle which were about to die out in his time. Records went back some 300 years. [c.1650]

1913 A small wild life park.

1950 Wild White cattle still there.

Possible Relationships:- CAMPSEA ASHE, STUDLEY ROYAL.

Note: Neither Bangor University nor the present owner Andrew Tennant have been consulted.

WELBECK ABBEY
Worksop, Nottinghamshire

The Duke of Portland K.G., P.C., K.C.V.O., b.1857

1894 Original stock presented by Mr. Whitaker of RAINWORTH HN p. 14.

c.1898 -1909 Rams provided from WENTWORTH WOODHOUSE.

1910 The Estates Manager, Alex Galbraith writing to Colonel Platt:-

'I wish to exchange our "Jacob Sheep" i.e. 4 shear ram for a shearling or two shear one – or I would purchase one if necessary – for the Duke of Portlands' Flock at Welbeck. Have you a pure "Jacob" ram with good head – two pairs of horns and of a good type, you could let me have for sale or exchange?'

1913 Had twenty ewes.

Relationships:- CHATSWORTH, BULSTRODE.

WENTWORTH CASTLE
Stainborough Worsborough, Barnsley, South Yorkshire

The Earl of Strafford – 1st creation 1711, b.1672

The Earl of Strafford, b.1772

1730 'Said to have been imported by the Earl of Strafford' Perhaps the origin of Captain Bruce Vernon-Wentworth's flock. [STAINBROUGH HALL]. HN p. 15.

WENTWORTH WOODHOUSE
Wentworth, Rotherham, South Yorkshire

A little wishful thinking and imagination is required for this entry. Mr. Heatley Noble writing in 1913 says:-

. . . 'I think it can be shown that by far the greater number [of piebald sheep] are direct descendants of the Wentworth [Woodhouse], Milton and Tabley flocks. Out of the fourty-one flocks records of which are appended, ten appear to date back to the Fitzwilliam family. . . it is more than probable that others of which the history is not known are derived from the same stock.'

Wentworth Woodhouse is Britain's largest classical stately home; its 606ft long Palladian facade also makes it Europe's longest stately home. The house dates back to 1630 when it was built for the Earl of Strafford to be largely rebuilt in the first half of the 18th Century for the Marquess of Rockingham.

The 3rd Earl Fitzwilliam who was born in 1719, married Lady Anne Watson-Wentworth in 1744; she was the eldest daughter of the Marquess of Rockingham. Their son born in 1748 was Lord Lieutenant of Ireland for a short time in 1795; he first married Lady Charlotte Ponsonby (see TABLEY) who's mother had been Lady Caroline Cavendish (CHATSWORTH). It will have been the 5th Earl, born in 1786 and his son born 1815 who's Estate papers were so well documented.

The first mention of Spanish sheep is for May 31st 1791.

    3 Spanish Wether Lambs
    1 Spanish Ewe Lamb

In October 2 'Spanish old wethers' were sold to Mr. Green of Northamptonshire for 6/- each; oddly enough he paid the same price for 'three Spanish ewes'. These sheep cannot have been Merinos, as at this period Merinos from Spain were selling at very high prices.

By August 1792 there were a total of 907 sheep, of which, listed at the end were:-

    5 Spanish old Wethers
    11 Spanish Ewes
    1 Spanish old Ram
    1 Spanish Ram Lamb
    4 Spanish Wether Lambs
    5 Spanish Ewe Lambs.

By November 1792 there were a total of 138 Bullocks, one entry of which reads:-

'6 large Bullocks from the Teams feeding'; in the same section, 20 Highland Bullocks 3 years old came in Aug 28th 1792 cost £83. 19s. 0d. whilst the same number at 4 years old in September cost £100. 0s. 6d.

Listed last of over 400 sheep were:-

    5 old Spanish Wethers
    11 old Spanish Ewes
    1 Spanish old Ram
    2 two year old Rams bought in Oct 1791
    1 two year old Ram bought Oct 30th 1792 at £5. 3s. 0d.
    1 one year old Ram bought Oct 30th 1792 at £2. 15s. 0d.
    3 Ram Lambs
    1 Spanish Ram Lamb
    4 Spanish Wether Lambs
    5 Spanish Ewe Lambs
    40 four year old Wethers from Buxton Oct 25th 1792 at 15s.
each.

It is not possible to tell if those with prices were 'Spanish'.

In 1793 '6 scotch Wethers sold to Michael Bisby of Wentworth at 21/-. £6. 9.s 0d.

In 1806, amongst the 72 Bullocks were:-

    '3 long horn'd Bullocks in Teams
    3 short horn'd Bullocks in Teams'

Amongst the 1092 sheep were:-

58 Spanish & large sheep to feed
30 Spanish sheep
13 Spanish lambs
38 Welch sheep
10 Forest sheep
12 Scotch sheep

In 1807, of the 993 sheep – the Spanish moving nearer the top of the list were:-

56 Spanish Sheep
2 Spanish Rams
4 Spanish Lambs

The following years are much the same figures; 1809 shows there were:-

'48 Spanish Ewes, Weathers, and Rams' out of 878 Sheep.

In 1810 there is 'An Account of Stock Belonging to the Right Honourable Earl Fitzwilliam on Sept 5th Under my Care' and signed Abel Eyre [sic], Shepherd. (See page 90)

He lists the various fields in which the sheep are to be found; as follows:-

Deer Park: Welch Sheep   43
Deer Park: Spanish Sheep   42
Deer Park: Lambs Spanish   12

Hage Paddock: aged tups 22   tup lambs 12   Spanish 7   41.

1810, out of a total of 853 sheep there were 39 Spanish Sheep
                                            12 Spanish Lambs.

XLII. 1834

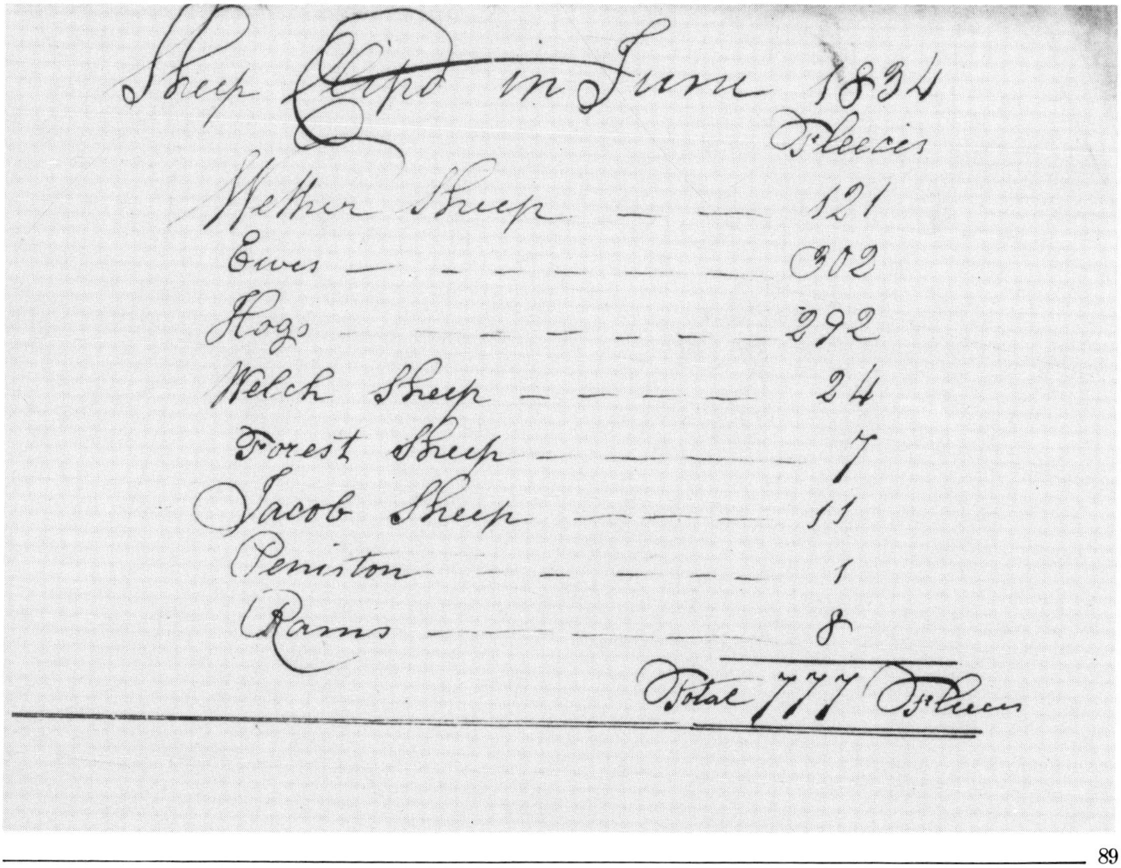

Sheep Clip'd in June 1834

Fleeces

Wether Sheep — — 121
Ewes — — — — — 302
Hogs — — — — — — 292
Welch Sheep — — — — 24
Forest Sheep — — — 7
Jacob Sheep — — — 11
Peniston — — — — 1
Rams — — — — 8

Total 777 Fleeces

The years 1812, 1813, 1817 and 1823 show very much the same proportion of Spanish sheep. What is interesting is that 1823 is the last year they are named Spanish; in 1834 (see page 89) out of a total of 777 sheep there are:-

Welch Sheep	24
Forest Sheep	7
Jacob Sheep	11
Peniston	1

The last of these beautifully written entries is for 1st Jan 1835 (Plate XLIII see below).

To Stock ewes	322
Lambs	298
Shearling Wethers	132
Fat – do –	48
Fat Ewes	18
Welch Sheep	33
Jacob Sheep	16
Rams	6
	873 Total

Signed A. Hare [sic] (See 1810 entry)

XLIII. 1835

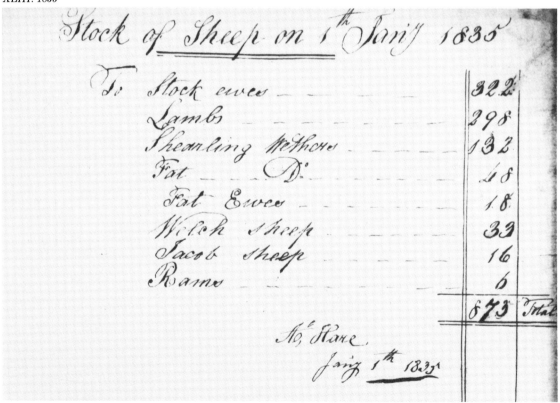

In the 1856 'List of Birds and Animals at the Menagerie' at Wentworth Woodhouse are listed '6 Demerara Sheep'. (Ref. WWM A 1425 Sheffield City Libraries.) These are headed 'Paddock Animalsa and include Llamas, and Alpaca, Cushmere goats, Kangaroos and an American Bear etc.

It is possible that these Demerara Sheep may have something to do with the fact that the original line of the Earls of Strafford stems from the son of The Hon. Robert Byng who was Governor of Barbados some 100 years earlier.

Writing to Colonel Platt in 1909, Mr. W. H. Wigfield of Home Farm, Wentworth (presumably the Estate Agent) tells how he has sent rams since 1898 to the following estates:- GORDDINOG, WESTON, Salop, MILTON, WIGGANTHORPE, NOBLETHORPE HALL, ABERCAIRNY, STAINBOROUGH HALL, CUSWORTH HALL, BRODSWORTH HALL, TONG HALL, WELBECK ABBEY and INGLEBOROUGH.

It is curious that Chatsworth is not in this list as Mr. Wigfield had started his letter by saying:-

'I find on enquiry the Ram you had from here last year was a Son of the Ram got from Chatsworth'.

It is also odd that he does not mention either Kilkenny or Shanbally Castles as Mr. Heatley Noble (p. 9) says:-

'Lady Constance Butler owns a flock of six breeding ewes which came from Wentworth in 1903.'

He also says:-

'The Earl of Fitzwilliam keeps a flock of twenty ewes. They have been at Wentworth a great number of years as shown by a picture by Stubbs about the year 1760.'

This wrongly attributed painting, and that at Tabley, have been the basis of a great deal of incorrect dating used by almost every author when trying to discover the origin of these sheep. Both pictures are reproduced on pages 17 & 80.

Note 1: Some people may be thinking that these Spanish sheep are Merinos. It is important to realise that at the time these sheep were flourishing at Wentworth huge prices were being asked for the true Merino – hardly 6/-. Equally they were kept in the Deer Park, presumably with the deer; and were never listed at the top of any inventory of sheep which would have been the case had they been valuable Spanish Merinos. See the description given on page 22, defining these two breeds of sheep in nearby Derbyshire for about this same era. Lastly, once 'Jacob' is used, 'Spanish' no longer appears.

Note 2: Wentworth Woodhouse was acquired by Mr. Wensley Haydon-Baillie a descendant of the Fitzwilliam family on 1st March 1989; he is a keen conservationist.

(Notes on the house taken from Daily Telegraph of 2.3.89.)

Relationships:- Already mentioned, together with:-
SCALFORD HALL, BRAMHAM PARK.

WEST HASLERTON HALL
Malton, North Yorkshire

Lt. Col. Cuthbert Dawnay
M.C., b.1891

Mrs. Cuthbert Dawnay
b.1897

Miss V. Elliott
(Mrs. Benthall)

1921 Brought her sheep from Maidwell with her upon marriage.

1963 Listed.

1969 Listed. J.S.S. No. 77.

1989 Listed. J.S.S. No. 77, with 20 ewes.

Relationships:- MAIDWELL, EYREFIELD, LEONARDSLEA, KNEPP.

WESTON
Plumpton,
Northamptonshire

Colonel, The Hon. Henry
Hely Hutchinson, b.1790

c.1841 Supplied Sir Henry Dryden [CANON'S ASHBY] with original sheep. Quoting from page 13 of Mr. Heatley Noble's article:-

'Mrs. Farrer [INGLEBOROUGH] writes to me "I may assure you on the authority of my aunts (daughters of Col. the Hon. H. Hely Hutchinson) that the origin of our flock is this: They were sent from the Cape by my Grandfather's military successor there to him soon after his marriage in 1823. The present Sir Alfred Dryden's [CANON'S ASHBY] flock were derived from this. My

Grandfather's were in the country before the sheep described by Sir Alfred as having been brought from Spain by an officer's wife. Sir Henry's account differs from that of his successor, Sir Alfred. From my earliest years I was always told my Grandfather gave some to Sir H. Dryden" '

Dryden's story is that the sheep came from Thorpe Manderville, 'several years before 1841.' HN p. 11.

In 1923 'M. Portal' of Holywell, Swanmore, Hampshire wrote to presumably Mr. Heatley Noble as follows:-

'A Mrs. Farrer wrote me hers came from the Cape when Hely Hutchinson was out there in about 1840 I fancy – he got 6 given in exchange for a piano – which sounds circumstantial evidence'

Relationships:- CUSWORTH, AVISFORD, INGLEBOROUGH, GARSCUBE.

WESTON PARK
Weston-under-Lizard,
Shifnal, Shropshire

The Earl of Bradford P.C.
b.1819

c.1910 Mrs. Maude, daughter-in-law of Sir George Maude writing to Mr. Heatley Noble says:

'The sheep you mention were (I think two ewes and a ram) given to Sir George Maude by the late Lord Bradford. . . .My husband, on the death of his father in 1894, sold them'.

In a further letter:-

'I remember the sheep arriving and being given by the late Lord Bradford, who was master of the horse to Sir George Maude.'
[Lord Bradford was Master of Horse 1874-1880 & 1885-1886.]

It would seem likely that these sheep went on to Sir John Barker in 1894 [GRANGE PARK].

1870 Stock from MILTON originally. HN p. 9.

c.1898 Rams provided from WENTWORTH WOODHOUSE.
-1909

1913 Listed as 14 ewes.

1953 Listed.

1964 Listed.

1969 J.S.S. No. 17.

THE WHARF
Market Overton, Oakham,
Rutland

Mrs. A. W. A. Smith

1964 Listed.

WHIPSNADE ZOO
Dunstable, Bedfordshire

Opened 1931

1933 April 22nd. Extract from The Times.
'Mottled Sheep from Bucks.'

Another very striking race of domestic animals to be seen at Whipsnade is the flock of piebald sheep in the paddock nearly opposite Cut-thro'-it-Wood, running with Japanese deer. The sheep were bought last year from the estate of Mr. Robert Vaughan near High Wycombe, where they had been for many years. They have thrived at Whipsnade and there are at present over a dozen lambs. The sheep are rather tall, with curly wool, and are mottled black and white, with a white blaze on the forehead. The rams tend to have four horns. They are generally known as Spanish sheep, and there are small flocks of them on several private estates in England. . .'

c.1938 Writing to the author in 1988, the present Lady Mansfield
-1943 [SCONE] had been told the following story by Mr. Black their retired Farm Manager:-

'. . . the original sheep did not actually come from Abercairney. The story is that the late Earl was shooting with Mr. Drummond-Moray

and indicated that he would like a few of the "spotted" sheep to graze around the Palace. Mr. Drummon-Moray had then said that he would have to get them from him because he had the only flock at the time. The Earl made a bet of £5 that he could get them elsewhere.

At the time he was a Director of Whipsnade Zoo and knew that they had some of the Jacob Sheep. He also knew that they wanted a Highland Bull so he swapped the Bull for a tup and 4 females thus winning his bet.

1963 The Director of the ASSINIBOINE PARK ZOO writing to Ex J.S.S. No. 601 told that:-

'The original group were imported from Whipsnade Zoological Park, Bedfordshire, England in 1963, and I believe they were the first to reach North America for many years.'

1964 Listed.

WHITEHOPE
Innerleithen, Peeblesshire,
Scotland

Miss Helen Hamilton

Inherited flock from Lullenden, East Grinstead.

c.1966 Had sheep from Colonel Enderby EGLINGHAM HALL.
Had sheep from Mrs. Bewicke, J.S.S. No. 49.

1967 Because of their interest in Belted Galloway, supplied EAST COOMBESHEND FARM with two Rams. J.S.S. No. 24.
Sold 'only ram lamb she had' to MAWBIE MAINS.

1968 Sold 5 ewes and a tup to BRENCHACHA.

1969 J.S.S. No. 63.

1989 J.S.S. No. 63.

WIGGANTHORPE HALL
Terrington, North Yorkshire

The Hon. Henry W.
Fitzwilliam, b.1840

c.1898 -1909 Rams provided by WENTWORTH WOODHOUSE.

1913 A flock of twelve to fourteen breeding ewes which came from WENTWORTH WOODHOUSE. HN p. 9.
Relationship:- SHANBALLY CASTLE.

WINSLOW HALL
Nr. Buckingham,
Buckinghamshire

Norman McCorquodale
C.B.E., J.P., b. c.1866

1909 Writing to Colonel Platt, Mr. Heatley Noble says:-

'I wrote to Alec McCorquodale who I know well, he tells me he has no sheep now, his father had a flock which were sold.'

Note: His son, Malcolm, who became Lord McCorquodale lived at COTSWOLD PARK.
Relationship:- LANSADURN.

WOLLATON HALL
Nottingham,
Nottinghamshire

The Lord Middleton, b.1817

1811 Sent 6 theaves and 3 lambs to CHADDESDEN. Ref. from 'A General View of the Agriculture and Minerals of Derbyshire' by James Farey (senr). Who says:-

'I have seen Spanish sheep in Gentlemen's Parks. . . these are of a dark brown colour spotted with white, with thick white tails, and they a good deal resemble some, that I have seen among the fancy stock in Gentlemens' Parks, and were called Cape Sheep.'
Relationship:- BRAMHAM PARK. See BILTON PARK
Note p. 40.

WOOD LANE FARM
Braunstone, Oakham,
Rutland

R. Baines

1964 Listed.

WYLD COURT **Hampstead Norris,** **Berkshire** *Sir William Cooke Bart.* *b.1873*	1923	Had sheep according to letter from M. Portal [HOLYWELL] to Eric Platt.
WYNDHAM PARK **Cromer, Norfolk** *J. Stubbins*	1964	Listed.

Information Required Please

Owners with sheep		**Ref.**
W. Balding	1915 GRANGE PARK Sale	
F. Bank	1915 GRANGE PARK Sale	
R. G. Baty	1915 GRANGE PARK Sale	
Thos Bossley	A 'local man' bought a total of 21 sheep from CHATSWORTH during the years 1804, 1806, & 1809.	Folios 36, 117, 31, 37
Mr. Bradley Firth	1900 had 30 breeding ewes from HN.	
Mr. Diggle	1909 had 30 ewes from Mrs. Noble [PARK PLACE].	HN p. 11
Walter Fenwick	1909. Writing to H.N. from Grosvenor Hotel, London re sheep in Ronda, Spain. Possible connection with Platt/Woollen Machinery/Dugdales took name of Fenwick, a 'Walter Fenwick' died 1903.	
William Hollins	1913 had small flock from Mr. Whitaker. 'Berry Hill, Manfield' listed by SH. Perhaps Mr. William Hollins of Burslem, Staffordshire?	HN p. 14
Irby The Rev. The Hon. L.R. C. (b.1822)	THE RECTORY, Whiston, Nr. Northampton. Possible connection with Col. Pratt as in 1852 his sister married Col. Pratt of Cabra Castle, Co. Cavan.	
Roy Lankester		Listed SH
Alfred Mansell & Co.	1915 GRANGE PARK Sale	
F. C. Selous, D.S.O. 1851-1917	'The African pied four-horned sheep' The Field, March 27th 1909. Well known explorer & hunter; in South Africa 1871-1881.	Listed SH See Werner
T. Towers		Listed SH
A. G. Watney	1915 GRANGE PARK Sale.	

The Epilogue

The conclusion gathered from the few strands of evidence collected for this History of the Jacob Sheep is that their unique markings, originally for camouflage, were carried by the majority of feral sheep from very early times throughout the world.

The many names by which these pied sheep have been known in the past inferred that they had come to the British Isles from overseas, usually a Mediterranean country. The two exceptions were the flock at TABLEY in Cheshire known as Persian, and the spotted Hungarian sheep at MONTREAL in Kent.

No evidence has been discovered that pied sheep were ever natives of the British Isles. Almost all the many breeds in this country take their names from geographic locations such as Southdown, Suffolk, St. Kilda, Black Welsh Mountain, Hampshire, Kent and Dorset Down, etc. The Dorset Horn may once have carried a 'spotted gene' as occasionally a black spot is still seen in their fleece, and when crossed with a Jacob the distinctive markings usually remain for the first generation. The black gene being dominant in the Jacob, (they are in reality a black sheep with white markings), black lambs are always the result when crossed with any other pure breed. Because the piebald characteristic is so liable to disappear through experimental or random breeding, by 1960 very few flocks of pure Jacob sheep existed in this country.

It is impossible to say that there is one definite location from which these sheep originated, but with the flourishing trade along the silk route from East to West it would seem that the blood of the spotted feral sheep of ancient Mongolia and China may still be carried in the pedigree of those flocks now so zealously tended today.

Pictorial Evidence

Two well-known artists painted flocks of pied sheep, in neither case has it been possible to find the location nor to discover the owner of the sheep. It is hoped with the publication of this book that some information will come to light.

THE ROSA BONHEUR PAINTING Plate XLIV

In 1857 Rosaline Bonheur, (1822-1899) the French artist, whilst on a visit to Scotland, painted another flock of sheep in a moorland setting. Her notes read:-

> *'troupeau de moutons au repos au milieu des bruyeres dans les montagnes d'Ecosse.' (A flock of sheep resting in the middle of moorlands in the mountains of Scotland.)*

In this peaceful picture, two rather poor specimens of Jacob sheep are shown in a flock of twelve sheep.

In 1872 this picture entitled 'Highland Sheep' was exhibited at Bethnal Green. It is now in the Wallace Collection and entitled 'Sheep in the Highlands'.

THE JAMES WARD PAINTING Plate XLV

In 1826 James Ward, R.A., (1769-1859) then living in London, but travelling the country to paint his many familiar portraits of animals, painted a flock of six Jacob sheep in a moorland setting.

Dr. Edward J. Nygren, Director of the Smith College Museum of Art, Northampton, Massachusetts, U.S.A. writes in June 1989:-

'Alas, I cannot suggest where the painting was executed. In fact, it probably was painted in Ward's London studio from sketches made years before the date of execution, even as early as 1800. It could well be Yorkshire.'

In an earlier letter dated 31st May 1989 he said:-

'Neeld does not appear in Ward's one surviving account book and his "Diary" does not extend to that date. Neeld did own a number of paintings by Ward however.'

This refers to a note on the back of the picture which reads:-

'John Neeld.Esq. gave this picture to Lt. Col. Wilson at Grittleton, 1st December 1832.'

The painting is monogrammed 'J. W. 1826'.

Sir John Neeld born in 1805 was Member of Parliament for Cricklade 1835-59 and for Chippenham 1865-68. He must have been aged 27 at the time of the presentation.

Nothing has so far been discovered about Colonel Wilson.

The commanding oil painting is of six Jacob sheep in a moorland setting with a church tower in the distance. It consists of two magnificently horned rams with perhaps a third ram in the background. One of these carries two horns, the other two rams are four-horned, one horn of which is badly fused. The three ewes, together with the rams, are nicely marked but with small, poor horns; all are badger-faced and have long tails.

Note: See TABLEY HOUSE for possible connection.

XLVI BILTON HALL c.1792

XLVII CHARLCOTE PARK 1989

XLVIII CHATSWORTH c.1981

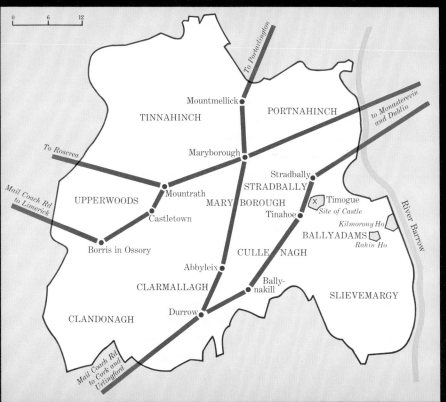

0   6   12

To Portarlington

Mountmellick

TINNAHINCH

PORTNAHINCH

to Monasterevin and Dublin

To Roscrea

Maryborough

Mail Coach Rd to Limerick

UPPERWOODS

Mountrath

Stradbally

STRADBALLY

MARY BOROUGH

Timogue

x Site of Castle

Castletown

Tinahoe

River Barrow

Kilmorony Ho

BALLYADAMS

Rahin Ho

Borris in Ossory

CULLE NAGH

Abbyleix

Bally-nakill

CLARMALLAGH

SLIEVEMARGY

CLANDONAGH

Durrow

Mail Coach Rd to Cork and Urlingford

XLIX

MAP OF QUEENS COUNTY

After Townlands six inch survey of 1841

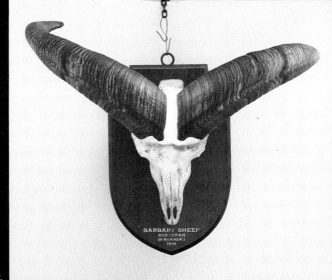

L Barbary Head 1912 A.D.

LI Yorkshire, c.1810.

LII German c.1731 A.D.

The First 100 Members
of the
Jacob Sheep Society
Founded in 1969

including information from the 1972 First Flock Book and the members, or their descendants,
who are still listed twenty years later.

J.S.S. NO.	NAME	SHEEP	J.S.S. NO.	NAME	SHEEP
	37 Cam Road			Cricket St. Thomas	
	Cambridge			Chard	
				Somerset	
1.	Miss Castleman-Brown, M.B.E.	None	8.	Major J. J. Ogilvie	13
	THE KNOLL FARM				
	Aldington			SHALSTONE MANOR	
	Ashford			Buckingham	
	Kent		8.	S. H. L. Purefoy	
2.	**The Lady Aldington**	12	9.	**G. Purefoy**	
Bought: Ewe from Mrs. Gladys Calthrop of Aldington;				Wissenden	
Sissinghurst stock.				Cooper's Lane	
Ewe from Mrs. A. R. Pym, Charing, Kent. Dam from				Sellindge	
Sissinghurst stock.				Ashford	
				Kent	
	SAHAM LODGE		10.	Mrs. Barbara Batt	2
	Saham Toney				
	Norfolk			Pilkington Farms	
3.	Miss H. Bartholomew	116		Offley Hoo	
				Hitchin	
	Princes Hotel			Herts	
	Bouverie Road		11.	Dickinson	56
	Folkestone				
	Kent			Doghouse Farm	
				Stone Street	
	Lady MacMichael			Petham	
4.	**The. Hon. Mrs. Roberts, M.V.O.**	None		Canterbury	
				Kent	
	CHARLECOTE PARK		12.	Peter M. Godden	14
	Warwick			*Ram from Mrs. J. Mount*	
5.	**National Trust**	75		*Bought: 5 Ewes from Mrs. J. Mount*	
	Street End Place			GARROWBY	
	Canterbury			York	
	Kent		13.	The Earl of Halifax	25
6.	J. Baker-White	7			
Bought: Ram from Lady Aldington				Squerryes Home Farm	
2 Ewes from Mrs. Mount, Canterbury, Kent				Westerham	
Ewes from Mrs. Garnham				Kent	
7.	**MILTON Estates Co.**	54	14.	Steven & Reynolds	15
	25 Priestgate			*Ram bred by Lady Aldington*	
	Peterborough				
	Earl Fitzwilliam				

bold — members or their descendants; capitals — see Flocks of Jacob Sheep in The British Isles; italic — information from the 1972 First Flock Book

Note: I am frequently asked why Miss Castleman-Brown is the first Member of the J.S.S. The reason is that it was she, in February 1969, who first
suggested that, as she now knew two people with Jacob Sheep we might as well start a Society. One was Miss Hermione Bartholomew and the other
the author, who had been corresponding with Miss Castleman-Brown on the subject of Peruvian Cavies. On 21st May the two ladies met at Audley
End Station for the first time and, sitting in the garden of an empty Public House addressed about 100 envelopes to potential Members. It was
decided to give Membership No. 1 to the originator of the idea.

J.S.S. NO.	NAME	SHEEP
	KNEPP CASTLE Horsham Sussex	
15.	Sir Walter and Lady Burrell	50
	RAVENDALE Higham Gobion Hexton Herts	
16.	**Mrs. M. Latimer** **Mr. and Mrs. J. H. Latimer**	30
	Bought: Ram from Mr. Shapland, Peppard, Henley-on-Thames	
	WESTON PARK Shifnal Shropshire	
17.	Earl of Bradford	45
	White House Blacklunans Blairgowrie Perth	
18.	H. Airth Grant	37
	Ennim Penrith Cumberland	
19.	Mrs. William Whitelaw	None
	CHATSWORTH Bakewell Derbyshire	
20.	Duke of Devonshire **The Duchess of Devonshire**	39
	Poplar Hall Brookland Romney Marsh Kent	
21.	John H. Paine	15
	Luton House Selling Faversham Kent	
22.	J. A. Swire	14
	CHIDEOCK MANOR Bridport Dorset	
23.	Lt. Col. H. J. G. Weld	39
	Bought: Ram from National Trust	

J.S.S. NO.	NAME	SHEEP
	EAST COOMBESHEAD FARM Harford Ivybridge Devon	
24.	Mrs. A. R. Matthews **Mrs. A. A. Matthews**	7
	Bought: Ram from A. J. Stanbury	
	CALSTONE Calne Wiltshire	
25.	**Mrs. P. Luard**	16
	Ram from Milton Estates *Bought: Ewe from Mr. Gent, Burbage*	
	Stone Farm Exford Minehead Somerset	
26.	Darby Haddon	30
	ARLINGTON COURT Killerton Estate Office Budlake Exeter Devon	
27.	R. E. Meyrick National Trust (**see 81**)	60
	Glan y foriog Farm Llanybyther Carmarthenshire	
28.	H. D. Jones	14
	BREACHMACHA Isle of Coll Argyll	
29.	**C. K. M. Stewart**	7
	Bought: Ram from A. Miller, Berwickshire	
	Department of Agriculture The University Reading Berks	
30.	Prof. J. C. Bowman	5
	LULWORTH CASTLE Farms Ltd. East Lulworth Dorset	
31.	C. G. Hyde	62
	Park Farm Sandon Scarborough Yorkshire	
32.	Paul Bryan, D.S.O., M.C., M.P.	None

bold — members or their descendants; capitals — see Flocks of Jacob Sheep in The British Isles; italic — information from the 1972 First Flock Book

J.S.S. NO.	NAME	SHEEP
	SCOTLAND LODGE Winterbourne Stoke Salisbury	
33.	R. Wales	50
	SCALFORD HALL Melton Mowbray Leicestershire	
	Mrs. Colman	
34.	**The Lady Wendy Lycett**	55
	Ardwell Gatehouse of Fleet Kirkcudbright	
35.	L. J. McCulloch	5
	Eeans Leaze Farm Witchampton Wimborne Dorset	
36.	J. R. Cotterell	None
	Woolton House Bekesbourne Canterbury Kent	
37.	Mrs. John Mount	13
	ORROLAND Dindrennan Kirkcudbright	
38.	Miss K. M. A. Clark	90
	Beachamwell Hall Swaffham Norfolk	
39.	Rex Carter Farms Ltd.	10
	Hardwick Hill Priors Hardwick Rugby Warwickshire	
40.	A. S. C. Grindley	6
	Coles Farm Box Wiltshire	
41.	Robin Morley	None
	Soggs Parva Ewhurst Robertsbridge Sussex	
42.	S. Hall	21
	Ram from Charlecote Park	

J.S.S. NO.	NAME	SHEEP
	THE OLD HOUSE Sutton Courtenay Abingdon Berkshire	
	J. F. B. Pomeroy	
43.	**Lady Heathcoat Amory**	13
	c/o Strutt & Parker 82 St. Ann Street Salisbury Wiltshire	
44.	G. L. H. Alderson	12
	CLOUGH HOUSE FARM Croft Wainfleet Lincs.	
45.	**Mrs. P. Caudwell**	4
	Ram from Miss Bartholomew	
	CHURCH FARM Ryme Intrinseca Sherborne Dorset	
46.	W. H. Batten	50
	Mill House Bethersden Ashford Kent	
47.	Mrs. R. Garnham	3
	LITTLE GLEMHAM c/o Flick & Son Old Bank House Saxmundham Suffolk	
	Lady Blance Cobbold	
48.	**Captain P. M. Cobbold**	23
	EGLINGHAM HALL Alnwick Northumberland	
49.	Mrs. Bewicke	40
	BRAMHAM PARK Boston Spa Yorkshire	
50.	Col. F. Lane Fox	None
	Westrig Ancrum Jedburgh Roxburghshire	
51.	Miss D. B. Mudie	2

bold — members or their descendants; capitals — see Flocks of Jacob Sheep in The British Isles; italic — information from the 1972 First Flock Book

J.S.S. NO.	NAME	SHEEP	J.S.S. NO.	NAME	SHEEP
	SCONE PALACE Perth			Marshside Farm Ruckinge Ashford Kent	
52.	Earl of Mansfield	30	62.	R. P. Collick	7
	Hunts Hill Farm Normanay Guildford Surrey			*Bought: Ram from Lady Aldington*	
53.	R. Hart	40		**WHITEHOPE** Innerleithen Peeblesshire	
	PARK FARM Finchingfield Braintree Essex		63.	**Miss Helen Hamilton**	102
				Bought: Ram from A. Redpath	
54.	Frank Loftus	30		**BROAD OAKS** Ludlow Shropshire	
	THE DEANERY Bampton Oxfordshire		64.	Mrs. G. E. Burgess	30
55.	Miss Marjorie Pollard, O.B.E.	50		**SOUTHFIELD** Charing Ashford Kent	
	Warp Farm Blyton Carr Gainsborough Lincolnshire		65.	**M. H. Pym**	25
56.	Mrs. M. L. Revill	24		**KILTON FOREST** Worksop Nottinghamshire	
	Round House Doddington March Cambridgeshire			T. Baddiley & Son Ltd.	
			66.	*Miss J. Baddiley*	47
57.	Albert Minett	10		Brogues Wood Farm Tenterden Kent	
	Green Skares **Linden Park** **Hawick** **Roxburghshire**		67.	Brogues Wood Farms Ltd.	
58.	Gordon S. Muir	3		Hardres Court Farm Canterbury Kent	
	Moor End Holmbrook Cumberland		68.	R. D. Neame	5
59.	Master John Wallbank (5)	6		Lochside North Roe Shetland Islands	
	Bought: Ram from Miss Bartholomew		69.	Alex Williamson	4
	Coval Hall Chelmsford Essex			Manor Farm Bawdsey Woodbridge Suffolk	
60.	Col. G. R. Judd	6	70.	N. E. Simper & Son Ltd.	5
	Capernwray New Farm Carnforth Lancashire			Watton Abattoir Brandon Road Watton Norfolk	
61.	A. J. Collinson	90	71.	G. D. Bowes & Son Ltd.	110

bold — members or their descendants; capitals — see Flocks of Jacob Sheep in The British Isles; italic — information from the 1972 First Flock Book

J.S.S. NO.	NAME	SHEEP		J.S.S. NO.	NAME	SHEEP
	Fairthwaite Park				(see 27)	
	Cowan Bridge				ARLINGTON COURT	
	Via Carnforth				Killerton Estate Office	
	Lancashire				Budlake	
72.	Miss R. P. Ogden	8			Exeter	
				81.	**National Trust**	115
	MILL BROW FARM				(J. O. Gaze)	
	Loughrigg					
	Ambleside				Oxhill Manor	
	Westmorland				Warwickshire	
	Miss A. Wood			82.	Mrs. G. Rodwell	15
73.	**Messrs. Wood & Hainsworth**	39				
	Bought: Ram from G. Purefoy				Kirkbank	
					Kelso	
	MAWBIE MAINS				Roxburghshire	
	Annan			83.	Mrs. Buist	4
	Dumfriesshire					
74.	**Mrs. Ella Maxwell**	14			PALACE HOUSE	
					Beaulieu	
	Glen Wye				Hampshire	
	Courtfield			84.	The Lady Montagu of Beaulieu	30
	Ross-on-Wye					
	Herefordshire				Skeet Hill Cottage	
75.	Mrs. J. H. Vaughan	11			Skeet Hill	
					Chelsfield	
	Whittlebury				Kent	
	Towcester			85.	**A. R. Aubrey**	3
	Northamptonshire					
76.	A. H. Marston	40			THE OLD RECTORY	
					Lighthorne	
	WEST HESLERTON HALL				Warwick	
	Malton				The Hon. Adam Butler	
	Yorkshire			86.	**The Rt. Hon. Sir Adam Butler**	6
	Miss Cuthbert Dawnay					
77.	**Miss V. Elliott**	20			The Manor	
	Bought: Ram from Miss Bartholomew				Poynings	
					Brighton	
	SOUTH BLAGDON FARM				Sussex	
	Thorndon Cross			87.	A. P. Lee	152
	Okehampton					
	Devon				Badlesmere Court	
78.	Harold E. Channess	21			Faversham	
					Kent	
79.	Stones (see 94)	25		88.	Miss Joy Scutt	17
	Kingscroft Farm				Twigside Farm	
	Bedhampton				Ibstone	
	Havant				High Wycombe	
	Hampshire				Buckinghamshire	
80.	Arthur Jeram	30		89.	D. C. Farrar	3
					COGDEN FARM	
					Burton Bradstock	
					Bridport	
					Dorset	
				90.	**R. F. Bailey**	59
					Bought: Ram from L. A. Burton	

---

bold — members or their descendants; capitals — see Flocks of Jacob Sheep in The British Isles; italic — information from the 1972 First Flock Book

J.S.S. NO.	NAME	SHEEP	J.S.S. NO.	NAME	SHEEP
	Great Meadow Castleton Isle of Man			Milstead Old Rectory Sittingbourne Kent	
91.	Lt. Col. R. H. D. Riggall	35	96.	Mrs. McCandlish	32
				Bought: Ram from Mr. Lee	
	REDENHAM PARK Andover Hampshire A. Kidstone			Grey Barn Angmering Littlehampton Sussex	
92.	**Mrs. N. M. D. Sheffield**	10	97.	Lt. Cdr. and Mrs. Pinsent	3
	Sherborne Castle Estates Digby Estate Office Cheap Street Sherborne Dorset			**KNOCKEROON** Barrhill Ayrshire G. Massey	
93.	G. B. Dawson	21	98.	**Mrs. M. Morren**	14
				Bought: 4 Ewes from Miss Clark	
	Plas Einion Llanfair D.C. Ruthin Denbighshire			Sheldon Manor Chippenham Wiltshire	
94.	Mrs. S. D. Stones (see 79)		99.	Major Martin Gibbs	35
	Ram bred by Miss Clark				
	Bought: 3 Ewes from Miss Hamilton, Innerleithen 2 Ewes from J. Russell, Inverness 3 Ewes from Mrs. J. T. Roberts			Knoyle Park Salisbury Wiltshire	
	Sherington Manor Selmeston Polegate Sussex		100.	Lady Eden	None
95.	F. Chandless	18			

Many flocks do not appear in any list. Those who joined the Jacob Sheep Society in subsequent years will be found in the Society's Handbooks, and their registered flocks in the Flock Books.

bold — members or their descendants; capitals — see Flocks of Jacob Sheep in The British Isles; italic — information from the 1972 First Flock Book

106

Jacob Sheep Society
1989

Patron:	H.R.H. Princess Alexandra, the Hon Lady Ogilvie, G.C.V.O.
President:	The Lady Aldington
Chairman:	Mrs. M. E. Leithead
Vice Chairman:	Mr. C. P. Moorhouse
Past Chairman:	Mr. R. F. Bailey
Field Officer:	Mrs. R. E. Blacknell
Consultant:	Mr. John Thorley
Hon. Treasurer:	Mr. John Earll
Secretary:	Mrs. John Earll
	The Pines, 242 Ringwood Road, St. Leonards, Ringwood, Hants BH24 2SB

Council

Scotland	England	Wales
Miss M. M. Graham	Mr. R. W. Brewis	Mr. W. M. Jones
Mr. E. A. Bundy	Mr. J. A. Milner	
Mr. J. Kirkland	Mr. N. R. Davis	
	Major D. Chetwode	
	Mr. D. E. Tuffney	
	Mrs. S. Sleightholme	

The Jacob Sheep Society Limited   Registered No. 1466040, England   Registered Charity No. 259858

Members of the
Jacob Sheep Society

A
Mr. R. Adams
Mrs. A. Adams
Mr. D. Adams
Mr. J. W. Adamson
Mr. G. Adamson
Mr. H. W. F. Adamson
Miss H. Agar
Miss E. Agate
HRH Sheika N. Al-Kalifa
Mrs. J. Alcock
Mrs. M. J. Alcroft
Major & Mrs. R. Alderson
The Lady Aldington
Mr. I. Alexander
Mrs. A. M. Alexander
Mrs. C. B. Alison
Mr. & Mrs. J. Allan
Mr. D. Allen
Mr. & Mrs. C. A. Allen
Mr. & Mrs. D. Amos
Mr. & Mrs. I. Anderson
Mr. G. Anderson
Mr. L. A. Anderton
Mrs. D. R. Angill
Miss L. Angill
Mr. A. Appleton
Mr. D. A. Arlett
Arlington Court
Mrs. P. Arnold-Forster
Mr. T. Ash
Mrs. C. M. K. Ashby
Mrs. E. Ashford
Mrs. E. Ashwin
Mr. J. Asijee
Mrs. I. Athey
Mr. G. Atkins
Mr. A. R. Aubrey
Mrs. E. A. Aubrey-Fletcher

B
Mrs. M. A. Backhouse
Mrs. S. Backhouse
Mr. & Mrs. N. Bacon
Miss J. Baddiley
Ms. J. Baden-Powell-Jones
Mr. R. F. Bailey
Mrs. H. Baillie
Mrs. J. Bain
Messrs. M. E. & R. S. Baines
Mr. B. F. Bakel
Mr. & Mrs. R. Baker
Mrs. P. M. Baker
Mr. H. A. Baker
Mrs. L. Ball
Mr. & Mrs. M. Ballard
Mr. & Mrs. D. Balmforth
Mr. M. A. V. Bankes-Jones
Mr. C. G. W. T. Banwell
Miss S. Banwell

Mrs. D. Barker
Mrs. B. P. Barnaby
Mr. & Mrs. D. Barnard
Mr. & Mrs. J. E. Barraclough
Mrs. G. M. Barry
Mrs. P. A. Barter
Mr. C. V. G. Basford
Miss J. D. Bassett
Miss B. Bassford
Mrs. E. Bateman
Dr. & Mrs. J. H. Baumer
Mr. G. A. W. Bawcombe
Mrs. S. M. B. Beach
Mrs. L. M. Beagley
Mr. M. W. Beal
Mr. & Mrs. A. S. Beard
Mr. F. J. Bedell
Mrs. S. Bedell
Mr. R. H. Beech
Mrs. R. Beecher
Mr. & Mrs. V. L. Beeching
Ms. J. M. Bell
Mrs. L. M. Bellerby
Mr. & Mrs. R. J. Bence
Mrs. G. B. Benfield
Mr. & Mrs. N. Berrisford
Mr. T. S. Bickle
Dr. M. Bilbrough
Bill Quay Community Farm
Association
Mrs. G. and Miss A. Billington
Messrs. G. T. & M. J. Bilverstone
Ms. M. J. Bilverstone
Mr. H. Binions
Mrs. J. Bishop
Mrs. D. Bishop
Mrs. E. Bishop
Mrs. P. Bissaker
Mr. W. H. Black, MBE
Mr. & Mrs. J. T. Black
Mr. B. Blacklay
Mrs. R. E. Blacknell
Mr. A. J. Blacknell
Mr. C. Boase
The Lady Anne Boles
Mr. S. Boon
Mrs. J. L. Boraston
Mr. N. Borg
Mr. A. Borthwick
Mrs. C. L. E. Boughey
Mr. P. Boughton
Mr. & Mrs. E. M. Bourgoin
Dr. B. N. and Mrs. M. Bowden
Miss R. Bowden
Mr. & Mrs. E. E. Bowyer
Mr. & Mrs. R. Brackenbury
Mrs. S. Bradbury
Mr. & Mrs. Bradeley
Mrs. J. K. Bradley
Mr. G. Brazendale, BSc

Mrs. J. M. Brazier
Miss P. Brenninkmeyer
Dr. & Mrs. R. W. Brewer
Mr. R. W. Brewis
Mr. & Mrs. M. R. Bridgeman
Mrs. A. Brillenburg-Wurth-Haaxman
Mr. & Mrs. R. Brinkman
Mr. R. P. Broad
Miss H. Brogren
Mrs. R. M. Bromley
Mr. P. R. Brooks
Mr. L. L. Brown
Mrs. P. M. Brown
Mrs. B. Brown
Messrs. A. E. Brown & Sons
Miss A. Bruten
Mr. P. G. Bruan
Mrs. C. Bryant
Mr. & Mrs. D. W. Bryant
Messrs. M. R. Byrne
Mr. M. J. Buckley
Mr. & Mrs. R. Buckley
Mrs. R. A. Budge
Mr. & Mrs. A. L. Bull
Mrs. I. Bull
Mr. & Mrs. E. Bundy
Mrs. A. Bundy
Mrs. P. Burgess
Mr. I. P. Burgess
Mrs. Burnett-Stuart
Mrs. A. Burnham
Mr. S. L. Burrough
Mrs. G. M. Burrows
The Rt. Hon. Sir Adam Butler
Mr. J. Butler
Mrs. P. Butler
Mrs. P. Butt

C
Mr. E. Cabalo
Mrs. M. A. W. Cairns
Mr. & Mrs. G. P. Calveley
Mr. J. E. Calvert
Mrs. S. D. Cambage
Mrs. J. Campbell
Mrs. H. M. Campbell
The Rt. Hon. The Viscount Camrose
Mrs. C. D. Carmichael
Mr. & Mrs. B. P. Carr
Mrs. J. A. Carr-Saunders
Lt. Cmdr. N. A. Carter
Mr. & Mrs. W. R. Carter
Mr. K. Cartwright
Mrs. A. Carver
Dr. & Mrs. J. Cash
Mr. & Mrs. J. Castle
Mr. & Mrs. Catlin
Mrs. P. Caudwell
Mr. & Mrs. K. D. Causer
Mr. E. Cawkwell

Mrs. E. J. Cawte
Mrs. S. D. Cazenove
Mrs. S. Chadburn
Mr. & Mrs. G. K. Chalk
Mrs. M. M. Chambers
Mrs. R. M. Chaplin
Mrs. J. A. Chapman
Mr. R. Chapman
Mr. & Mrs. R. Chappell
Chatsworth Farms
Mr. & Mrs. R. G. Cheesman
Mr. F. Cheffings
Mrs. R. Cherry
Mrs. J. K. Cherry
Chessington Zoo
Mrs. J. V. Chesworth
Major G. D. Chetwode
Mrs. A. C. Chillingworth
Mrs. G. Ching
Mrs. S. Christie
Mrs. R. Christodolo
Mr. & Mrs. M. J. Chudley
Mr. & Mrs. W. V. Church
Mrs. S. M. Cianchi
Misses Y. & M. C. Claessens
Mrs. M. Clark
Mr. & Mrs. J. I. Clark
Mr. J. Clark
Mrs. E. Clarke
Mr. A. Clarke
Messrs. Clarke & Miller
Mr. G. H. C. Clay
Mrs. M. Clouston
Capt P. M. Cobbold
Mrs. E. Colling
Mrs. M. Collingham
Mr. & Mrs. P. M. Collings
Mr. C. St. J. Colthurst
Messrs. Connor & McPhie
Mrs. N. G. Cook.
Mrs. J. M. W. Cook
Mrs. J. E. Cook
Mrs. E. A. Copeland
Mr. & Mrs. S. J. Copeland
Miss J. Coppins
Mrs. P. R. Corri
Mr. D. Corrigan
Mrs. M. Costin
Mrs. E. M. Cotton
Mrs. E. M. Coulthard
Ms. S. Cousins
Mr. R. J. Coward
Mr. J. M. Coward
Mrs. R. H. R. Cox
Mr. K. A. Cox
Mrs. G. Cox
Mr. & Mrs. Coxhead
Mrs. G. E. Coyne
Mr. & Mrs. J. Craddock
Miss J. Craig
Mrs. R. Creemer
Mrs. H. Cripps
Miss J. Critchlow
Mrs. F. E. D. Crook
Mrs. A. Crosland
Mrs. A. M. Cross
Mr. G. E. M. Cross
Mr. M. R. S. Crow

Mr. D. J. Crowdell
Capt & Mrs. G. Crowden
Mr. & Mrs. W. Crowe
Mrs. J. M. M. Crozier
Mr. J. A. Crump
Mrs. V. E. Crump
Miss J. F. Crump
Mrs. N. Cunliffe-Lister
Miss K. Cunningham
Mr. & Mrs. I. C. Curd
Mr. & Mrs. R. Curle
Mrs. J. V. M. Curry
Mr. J. M. Curtis
Mr. S. H. Curtis

D
Mrs. M. Da Cunha
Dr. J. Daly
Mr. & Mrs. K. M. Daniel
Mr. D. Daniell
Mrs. L. Daniels
Mr. G. Dann
Miss L. Darbison
Mrs. C. M. Dare
Mrs. P. Davey
Miss M. I. M. Davidson
Mr. G. Davies
Mr. & Mrs. R. P. Davies
Mr. D. G. Davies
Mr. D. S. Davies
Mr. & Mrs. D. S. Davies
Mr. & Mrs. J. Davies
Mr. & Mrs. T. Davies
Mrs. E. T. M. Davies
Messrs. N. R. & S. M. Davis
Mr. R. W. Davis
Mrs. J. Davis
Mr. R. J. Davis
Mrs. B. de Capell Brooke
Miss E. de Righi
Miss S. de Sarigny
Mrs. I. A. de Wilton
Mr. J. W. de-Kulik
Mr. & Mrs. C. Deacon
Mrs. R. Deacon
The Lady Deedes
Mrs. A. Denholm
Mr. & Mrs. C. H. Dennis
Mr. & Mrs. R. Deppa
The Duchess of Devonshire
Mr. D. Diamond
Mrs. K. Dick
Mr. J. Dicker
Mr. P. R. Dickinson
Mrs. A. G. Dickinson
Messrs. F. Dickson
Mrs. J. Diebel
Mr. O. J. Diggle
Mrs. O. J. Diggle
Mrs. J. M. Digweed
Mr. L. M. S. van Dijk
Mr. & Mrs. D. F. C. Dingle
Mrs. P. C. Dix
Dr. & Mrs. T. P. Dixon
Messrs. Dixon & Hughes
Mrs. E. H. Dockray
Miss C. H. Dodd
Mr. & Mrs. J. D. Dodsworth

Miss E. J. Dodsworth
Mr. S. J. Dodsworth
Mrs. M. Doig
Mrs. P. Donald
Mr. I. Donaldson
Miss D. E. Done
Mrs. S. M. Dorrell
Mrs. M. Dossor
Mrs. F. Douetil
Mrs. R. Douglas
Mrs. M. Douthwaite
Mr. & Mrs. M. J. Dowding
Miss D. Dowell
Mr. D. M. Downie
Mrs. E. Downie
Mrs. H. Drew
Mr. W. G. S. H. Drummond-Moray
Mr. & Mrs. R. D. Dudley
Ms. S. Duffen
Mrs. R. Dunsmore
Mr. B. Durrant
Miss B. E. Dyson
Mrs. A. C. Dyson

E
Mrs. C. E. Earnshaw
Mrs. J. P. East
Mr J. A. East
Mrs. B. A. M. Eastwood
Mrs. D. S. D. Eckley
Mrs. C. A. Edden
Mr. M. Eden
Miss J. Edmondson
Mrs. S. A. Edwards
Mrs. A. J. Edwards
Mrs. J. R. Edwards
Lord Eglinton
Mr. T. Elcock
Miss V. Elliott
Dr. D. M. Elliott
Mr. & Nrs. G. H. C. Ellis
Mrs. K. L. Emerson
Mrs. C. Emery
Messrs. Emmett & Henderson
Miss V. Entwistle
Mrs. A. Evans
Mr. & Mrs. E. Evans
Mrs. M. Evans
Mrs. E. Evans Lombe
Ewar Stud Farms Ltd
Mrs. D. Ewers

F
Mrs. Falvey Leese
Mrs. C. Fane
Mr. & Mrs. D. O. Farmer
Mr. & Mrs. M. T. Fathers
Mrs. M. Faulder
Mrs. A. Fawcett
Mrs. S. M. Feltham
Mrs. J. M. Fenn
Mrs. A. Ferguson
Mr. A. W. F. Ferris
Mr. & Mrs. K. J. Field
Fieldwood Farm
Mr. C. E. Fiford
Mr. A. D. Finch
Mrs. R. G. M. Finn

Mrs. J. E. Fitch
Mrs. F. C. Fleming
Dr. D. R. M. Fleming
Mrs. J. F. Fletcher
Mr. & Mrs. M. G. Fletcher
Mrs. M. Flintoff
Mrs. E. Forbes
Mrs. E. Forbes-Robertson
Mrs. E. G. Ford
Mr. M. E. Ford
Mrs. J. V. Forster
Mrs. K. E. Fortescue
Ms G. R. Fortnum
Mr. W. F. Foster
Mr. & Mrs. J. R. Fozzard
T. Frame & Sons
Mr. & Mrs. F. France
Mr. & Mrs. A. France-Jaskowski
Mr. & Mrs. C. C. Franklin
Mr. A. Fraser
Mr. M. C. Freeman
Mrs. M. A. Freeth
Miss J. Frost
Mrs. M. A. Froud
Mrs. J. Fryer
Mr. A. G. Fuller
Mrs. B. Fullwood
Mrs. E. D. Furley
Mrs. G. M. Furney
Mrs. S. Furnival

G
Miss B. C. Gabb
Mrs. K. H.Gairdner
Mr. J. D. Gale
Miss J. A. Gamblin
Miss J. Ganderton
Mrs. M. M. D. Gardner
Mrs. H. W. Gardner
Mrs. W. A. Gartlan
Messrs. W. Gent
Mr. P. Gerrish
Mr. & Mrs. A. Gibb
Mrs. H. Gibson
Mrs. A. M. Gilbert
Messrs. D. & R. Gilbert
Mr. S. N. Gilbey
Mr. A. Giles
Mrs. P. Giles
Mrs. R. Gillam
Mrs. L. Gillett
Mr. D. Godley
Mrs. W. Godwood
Mrs. M. T. Golden
Mr. P. Goldsmith
Mrs. A. A. Gonnet-Hill
Mrs. H. Goodall
Miss S. Goodfellow
Mr. & Mrs. A. H. J. Goodwell
Mr. R. J. Goodwin
Mr. & Mrs. R. G. Gorton
Mrs. R. A. Gosling
Mr. T. N. Gover
Messrs. M. & R. Graham
Mr. R. M. Graham
Miss A. G. Graham
Mr. J. J. Graham
Mr. & Mrs. S. T. & Miss A. Grainger

Mrs. J. Grant
Mr. H. W. Green
Mrs. S. E. Green
Mr. D. Green
Mrs. J. Greene
Mr. K. Gregory
Mr. P. K. Gridley
Mrs. R. Grierson
Ms. M. Griese
Mrs. P. A. Grieve
Mr. D. M. Griffiths
Mrs. Griffiths
Mr. L. I. Griffiths
Mr. J. W. Grimshaw
Lt. Cdr K. A. Gristy
Mr. A. T. Guard
Mrs. V. Guiness
Mrs. R. E. Gunn
Dr. J. D. Gurney
Mr. & Mrs. D. T. Guy
Mrs. D. Guymer

H
Mrs. M. Haggard
Mr. D. Haigh
Mr. & Mrs. J. Haines
Mrs. C. N. Hainsworth
Mr. & Mrs. M. A. Hall
Messrs. A. G. S., E. & J. M. Hall
Mrs. C. V. Haller
Mrs. J. Hallett
Miss H. B. Hamilton
Major & Mrs. P. J. S. Hamilton
Mr. & Mrs. P. Hamlyn
Mrs. E. M. Hampson
Mr. W. T. Hanbidge
Mrs. S. H. Handley
Handweavers Studio
Mr. H. M. Hansford
Mr. R. S. Harding
Mr. & Mrs. B. P. Harding
Mrs. A. S. Hardy
Miss Lucy Hare
Miss W. Hargreaves
Mr. & Mrs. N. F. Harman
Mr. & Mrs. Harmsworth
Mr. M. W. Harper
Sqn Ldr. B. J. Harper
Mr. & Mrs. Harriman
Mrs. M. A. Harris
Carole & Stephen Harrison
Mrs. J. Hart
Mr. H. Hart
Mrs. F. M. M. Hartland-Mahon
Messrs. Hartley & Greenbank
Mr. M. Hartley
Harvestime Fellowship
Mr. & Mrs. L. R. Harvey
Mr. & Mrs. J. C. S. Hatch
Mrs. C. D. Hatcher
Mrs. K. E. S. Hawkins
Dr. R. K. M. Hay
Mr. B. Hayes
Mr. D. Hayward
Mr. & Mrs. M. Haywood
Mr. & Mrs. P. C. Haywood
Mrs. J. M. & Mr. A. B. Heald
Mr. A. Heath

Mrs. S. Heathcoat Amory
Lady Heathcoat Amory
Mr. & Mrs. D. Heathcote
Heckington & District Agricultural
  Society
Mr. R. Henderson
Mr. & Mrs. J. Hendy
Mrs. V. Henness
Mr. J. L. Henson
Mrs. J. Hewison
Mrs. M. Heywood
The Hon. Mrs. J. H. Heywood-
Lonsdale
Mr. J. D. Heyworth
Dr. C. F. Hider
Miss M. G. Higgin
Mr. & Mrs. F. F. Higgins
Mr. & Mrs. N. J. Higgins
Mrs. J. M. S. Hill
Mr. & Mrs. R. J. Hill
Mrs. V. Hill
Mrs. H. H. Hilsdon
Mrs. J. J. Hinds
Mr. B. T. Hinks
Ms. V. Hirsch
Mr. & Mrs. Hobden
Mr. E. C. F. G. Hodge
Mr. M. J. Hodgson
Mr. E. Hogben
Mr. & Mrs. T. Holder
Ms. J. Holder
Mrs. E. A. Holdich
Mr. B. V. Holgate
Mrs. E. M. Holgate
Mrs. P. Holloway
Mr. & Mrs. Holms
Mr. & Mrs. M. W. Homer
Mr. & Mrs. B. L. Hooker
Mr. B. M. E. Hope
Mr. & Mrs. J. R. Hopkins
Mrs. M. Horan
Mr. R. Horne
Mr. D. Horne
Mr. & Mrs. C. R. Hosking
Mr. & Mrs. K. E. Houghton
Mrs. R. Howell
Mr. & Mrs. Howell
Mrs. C. Howkins
Mr. & Mrs. A. Hudson
Mrs. A. W. Hughes
Mrs. A. Hughes
Mrs. L. I. Hughes
Mr. W. Hughes
Mr. N. Hughes-Onslow
Mrs. C. A. Hull
Mrs. C. M. Humphrey
Mrs. S. N. Humphreys
Lady K. Hunloke
Mr. & Mrs. R. J. Hunt
Mrs. V. Hunter
Mr. & Mrs. H. Hunter
Miss G. Hurcomb
Major M. W. G. Hurford
Mrs. K. B. Hurst
Mrs. L. A. Hurt
Mr. & Mrs. R. W. Husband
Mr. N. H. Hutchinson
Mr. C. G. Hyde

I

Miss P. S. A. Image
Mr. J. Inglis
Miss M. Irvine
Mrs. E. J. S. Isaac
Mrs. R. Ivory

J

Mrs. K. M. Jackson
Mrs. D. Jackson
Mrs. J. M. Jackson
Mrs. L. Jackson
Captain D. M. Jacobs
Mr. & Mrs. A. E. Jacobs
Mr. & Mrs. R. W. Jaggard
Miss R. I. James-Phillips
Lady Jardine Paterson
Mr. P. A. Jeffery
Mr. P. B. Jenkins
Col. D. H. Jenkinson
Mrs. M. E. Jennaway
Mrs. J. M. Joel
Miss B. G. Johnson
Mr. G. L. Johnson
Mr. & Mrs. J. L. Johnson
Mr. G. Johnson
Mrs. M. Johnson
Lt. Col. R. Johnson-Ferguson
Mrs. B. Johnston
Miss D. Johnston
Mrs. M. Johnston
Mrs. M. R. Johnstone
Mrs. W. A. Johnstone
Mr. & Mrs. R. G. Joice
Mrs. A. Jolliffe
Mr. & Mrs. D. P. Jones
Mrs. H. E. Jones
Lt. Comdr. C. W. B. Jones
Mr. H. L. Jones
Mrs. M. F. Jones
Mrs. R. O. Jones
Mr. R. W. Jones
Mr. H. Jones
Miss E. Jones
Mr. J. J. Jones
Dr. T. A. Jones
Mr. C. Jones
Mrs. H. W. Joynt

K

Mr. & Mrs. R. D. Kamel
Mrs. A. Kay
Mrs. L. J. Keating
Mrs. C. Keats
Miss A. M. Keats
Mr. D. S. M. Keddie
Miss H. J. Kelle
Rev. S. Kelly
Miss S. F. Kelsall
Mrs. Z. L. Kelton
Mrs. J. P. Kendal
Mrs. Kennedy
Mrs. A. M. Kennedy
Mrs. J. Kenning
Mr. H. Kiddy
Mr. A. R. Kilmartin
Messrs. Kimberley & Dawson
The Lord John King

Mrs. R. Kirby
Mr. & Mrs. J. Kirkland
Mrs. H. Kirwan
Miss M. Kittermaster
Mrs. R. Kitto
Ms. A. Kivell
Mrs. M. J. Knowles
Mrs. M. Knox
Mr. R. K. Kobayashi
Mrs. E. M. Kopley
Mrs. M. E. Kyles

L

Mr. & Mrs. D. Lacey
Mrs. B. A. Lamb
Mr. & Mrs. G. Lambert
Mr. K. J. Lambert
Mrs. R. M. Lane
Mrs. S. L. Lane
Mr. G. Lane Fox
Langdon Farms
Mrs. L. Langford
Langley Park Farming Co.
Mrs. A. Lasseter
Mr. & Mrs. J. H. Latimer
Mr. & Mrs. T. R. E. Latter
Mrs. E. Laurence
Mr. & Mrs. J. W. Lawday
Mr. D. J. Lawrence
Mr. H. W. le Boutillier
Mr. & Mrs. F. Lea
Mrs. M. E. Leake
Mr. J. R. Leaman
Miss H. Lee
Leeds City Council
Mrs. J. Legge
Mrs. F. E. Legge
Mrs. J. Leighton
Mrs. M. E. Leithead
Mr. P. E. R. Leney
Mr. & Mrs. B. J. Leppard
Mr. M. G. Leslie
Mr. D. Lewin
Messrs. Lewin & Adams
Mrs. J. Lewis
Miss E. Lewis
Mr. P. Lewis
Mrs. J. Lezemore
Mr. J. R. Liddiment
Mrs. L. A. Lillywhite
Dr. D. R. Lincicome
Mr. A. G. S. Lindon
Dr. & Mrs. P. Lindsell
Little London Spinners
Mrs. G. J. Littlechild
Mr. & Mrs. T. H. Lloyd
Mrs. M. Lloyd-Jones
Lochnaw & Garchrie Farming
Mr. K. R. Lock
Mr. R. Locker
Mr. & Mrs. K. Lockyer
Mr. P. Lohmeyer
Mr. & Mrs. P. J. Long
Mrs. M. D. Long
Miss S. Long
Mr. J. T. Long
Mr. J. G. Longstaff
Mrs. F. Loveday

Mr. E. H. Lovegrove
Miss A. E. Lovel
Mrs. J. Lovett
Mr. J. R. Lowe
Mr. & Mrs. D. C. Lowther
Mrs. P. J. Luard
Mr. N. H. J. Lucas
Mr. J. F. Lucas
Mrs. B. Luckhurst
The Lady Wendy Lycett

M

Mr. & Mrs. J. P. Mabbs
Mr. J. S. Macaskie
Mr. & Mrs. M. MacCurrach
Mrs. M. B. H. MacDonald
Mrs. J. MacIsaac
Mrs. A. Mackay
Mr. J. A. S. Mackenzie-Grieve
Mrs. D. C. Macmaster
Mrs. K. McPhail
Mrs. N. M. C. MacPherson
Mrs. J. E. Madeley
Mrs. J. L. Madeley
Mrs. M. A. Mainhood
Mr. & Mrs. P. Mansell
Mr. & Mrs. R. W. Margetts
Mr. & Mrs. P. G. Marks
Mr. P. J. Marlow
Mrs. W. Marsh
The Lady Joan Marshall
Mrs. L. G. Marshall
Mrs. J. S. Marsland
Mrs. P. Mason
Mrs. V. Mason
Mr. & Mrs. L. Masterman
Mr. & Mrs. L. Masterton
Miss K. M. Mather
Mrs. A. A. Matthews
Mrs. E. Maxwell
Mr. J. D. May
Mr. M. J. Mayes
Mrs. A. McDermott
Dr. & Mrs. D. J. S. McIlveen
Mrs. S. M. McLeich
Mrs. G. McLellan
Mr. D. McMillan
Mr. R. M. McMillan
Mr. A. J. Mercer
Mr. B. A. Meredith
Mr. & Mrs. M. T. Merrett
Mr. R. E. Metcalf
Mr. & Mrs. A. Metcalf
Mrs. W. Metson
Dr. N. P. Meyer
Mrs. S. Michael
Mr. & Mrs. M. I. Middlehurst
Mrs. M. Middleton
Mr. W. Middleton
Mrs. C. H. Miller
Mr. F. J. Miller
Mrs. A. C. Miller-Jones
Mrs. J. Milliken
Mrs. H. P. Mills
Mrs. J. B. Milne
Mr. & Mrs. J. K. Milner
Mr. J. K. Milner
Milton (Peterborough) Estates

Miss D. F. Mitchell
Mr. P. Mitchell
Mrs. T. M. Mitchell
Mrs. J. M. Moffat
Mr. & Mrs. A. Moffatt
Mrs. D. Molloy
Mr. R. P. M. Moncreiff
Mr. F. C. Montague
Mr. & Mrs. N. Moore
Mr. C. P. Moorhouse
Miss A. Moorhouse
Miss C. A. Moreby
Miss E Morgan and Miss S. Harries
Mrs. C. Morgan
Master G. Morgan
Miss B. J. Morley
Mrs. M. Morren
Mrs. D. E. Morris
Mrs. P. S. E. Morris
Mrs. G. F. Morrish
Mrs. J. S. Morse
Mr. W. M. Mostyn-Jones
Mr. & Mrs. Moxley
Mr. & Mrs. N. R. Mrozek
Mrs. B. A. Mole

N
Mrs. L. M. Nash
National Trust
National Trust
Mr. & Mrs. M. F. Naughton
Naylor-Moore Partnership
Mr. & Mrs. W. J. Neale
Mrs. R. Neblung
Mrs. P. M. Nelmes
Mr. J. Newborough
Mr. R. Newns
Mrs. M. I. Newton
Mrs. M. H. Niblock
Mr. & Mrs. C. Nicholls
Mrs. E. A. Nicholls
Mrs. P. Nichols
Mr. & Mrs. P. J. Nichols
Mrs. M. J. Nicholson
Mrs. I. S. Nicolson
Mrs. A. M. Nielsen
Mr. D. B. Nolan
Mr. & Mrs. R. A. Norris
Mr. R. J. Nottingham
Mr. H. Noyes
Mr. P. Nugent
Mrs. J. L. Nunn

O
Mr. & Mrs. O'Connell
Mrs. E. O'Driscoll
Mrs. J. A. O'Riordan
Mrs. M. O'Rourke-Jones
Mr. F. D. Oakeley
Mr. A. Oakes
Mr. A. Oakes
Mrs. S. J. Oakley
Mr. C. Oakley
Mr. J. R. H. Oddy
Mr. R. Odwyn
Mr. J. F. B. Oldham
Mr. C., W. Olds
Mrs. H. Osgerby

Mr. & Mrs. B. Osman
Mrs. J. Ovens
Mrs. M. E. Oxby

P
Mrs. I. Painter
Mr. & Mrs. T. A. Palmer
Mrs. L. J. Palmer
Mr. N. F. Palmer
Miss L. Pan
Mrs. J. M. Parfitt
Mrs. E. Parfitt
Mrs. P. Parker
Mr. D. N. Parkes
Mr. D. A. Parry
Mrs. V. R. de C. Parsons
Mrs. C. A. Parsons
Mr. & Mrs. D. G. Partridge
Mr. & Mrs. C. R. Pascall
Mr. & Mrs. D. R. Patterson
Mr. P. G. Paxton
Mr. C. Pearcy
Mr. M. Pearse
Mrs. A. Pearson
Mr. W. J. B. Peat
Mr. R. J. Peckham
Mrs. V. Pelmore
Mr. & Mrs. Pencherz
Mrs. D. Pendry
Miss A. Petitpierre and Mrs. M. Miles
Miss G. Petrie
Major & Mrs. C. R. Philipson
Mr. & Mrs. R. G. Phillips
Mr. & Mrs. J. D. Phillips
Mrs. D. B. Philps
Pilsdon Community
Mrs. Pirnie
Mrs. S. Pitt
Mr. M. W. A. Pitts
Mrs. L. Pollard
Mr. & Mrs. R. J. H. Pollen
Mr. D. J. Ponting
Mrs. A. Pook
Mr. M. J. Poole
Mrs. M. V. Pooley
Mr. & Mrs. P. R. Potten
Mr. H. M. Potts
Mrs. E. A. Power
Mr. M. Preller
Mr. C. H. Prentis
Mrs. H. F. Prescott
Mrs. D. J. Price
Mrs. D. A. Price
Mr. & Mrs. S. J. Pullen
Mr. & Mrs. M. Pullin
Mrs. D. M. Pulvertaft
Mr. S. H. L. Purefoy
Mr. G. P. Purefoy
Mrs. G. E. Purser
Mr. M. H. Pym

Q
Mr. C. W. Quick
Mr. & Mrs. Quick

R
Mrs. M. G. Rae
Mr. & Mrs. R. M. Raikes

Mr. J. Randall
Mr. & Mrs. D. A. Rawlings
Mr. & Mrs. R. Rawlingson
Mr. & Mrs. A. Rayner
Miss T. Read
Mrs. L. Redfern
Mr. & Mrs. P. J. Redman
Mr. A. Redpath
Mr. & Mrs. J. G. Reed
Mrs. B. Rees
Mrs. J. E. A. Rees
Mrs. J. C. Regan
Mr. & Mrs. P. A. Restan
Mrs. D. M. Rettie
Mrs. P. Reynolds
Mrs. R. Rhodes
Messrs. D. T. & W. T. Richards
Mr. W. T. Richards
Mrs. M. M. O. Richards
Mrs. D. A. Richardson
Mrs. J. Richardson
Mr. C. Richardson
Mr. & Mrs. P. K. Richardson
Messrs. Richardson & Simpson
Mrs. Ridd
Mrs. A. M. Robb
Mrs. J. E. Robb
The Hon. Mrs. Roberts
Mrs. J. Roberts
Mrs. V. Roberts
Mr. C. Roberts
Mrs. L. G. Roberts-Todd
Dr. G. Robertson
Mr. & Mrs. J. A. Robertson
Mr. & Mrs. R. A. Robinson
Mr. & Mrs. T. Robinson
Mrs. J. Robinson
Mrs. P. Robinson
Mr. & Mrs. D. G. Robinson
Mrs. J. Robinson
Mr. A. Robinson
Mr. D. I. Robson
Mrs. B. Robson
Mr. & Mrs. M. Rockliffe
Mrs. H. A. Rogers
Mr. D. de W. Rogers
Mrs. S. Roocroft
Major & Mrs. G. A. Rose
Mrs. J. Rose
Mr. M. Rosenberg, CBE
Mrs. J. Rosenthal
Mr. & Mrs. N. Rosier
Mr. S. Ross
Mrs. H. J. C. Ross-Skinner
Mrs. E. A. Row
Mrs. M. A. Rowberry
Miss M. Rowlands
Mr. & Mrs. D. R. Rowse
Mr. W. Roy
Mrs. A. Ruck-Keene
Mr. & Mrs. P. A. Rudd
Mrs. D. Ruscombe-King
Mr. & Mrs. M. L. Rushbrooke
Mr. J. Russell
Mrs. A. Rust
Mr. M. Ryan

S

Mrs. S. L. Salmon
Mrs. S. E. Salter
Mr. H. S. Sandelands
Mrs. B. Sanders
Mr. & Mrs. M. J. Saunders
Mrs. B. E. M. Saunders &
  Mrs. N. B. McVeigh
Mrs. J. H. Savage
Mrs. J. Scholes
Mr. J. Schyf
Mr. & Mrs. N. P. Scott
Mr. J. W. E. Scott
Mr. G. V. Seanor
Mr. & Mrs. J. D. R. Sears
Mr. D. Sears
Mr. & Mrs. Sebire
Mr. & Mrs. J. B. Secrett
Mr. C. Seddon
Mrs. A. J. Sellar
Mrs. B. Sellar
Mr. & Mrs. A. W. Seller
Mr. I. G. S. Sellers
Mr. H. R. Shackell
The Countess of Shaftesbury
Ms. C. L. Sharpley
Mr. V. A. Shatford-Butcher
Messrs. R. Shaw-Browne & Sons
Mr. J. M. Sheard
Mr. & Mrs. J. B. Shearer
Mrs. N. M. D. Sheffield
Messrs. J. W. Shemwell & Son
Lt. Col. J. H. Shepherd
Mrs. G. Sheperd
Mr. & Mrs. F. H. Shirley
Mr. & Mrs. P. Short
Ms. J. H. Showering
Sidmouth College
Mrs. P. M. Silke-Lindsell
Mrs. B. M. Simpson
Mrs. C. Simpson
Mr. D. Sizer
Mr. D. A. Skeet
Dr. & Mrs. R. F. Skinner
Mr. T. Slade
Mrs. C. D. Slater
Mr. I. Sleightholme
Mrs. S. Sleightholme
Mr. P. Sleightholme
Mr. J. Sleightholme
Master Ross Sleightholme
Miss J. F. M. Smedley
Mr. & Mrs. P. F. Smith
Mrs. C. Clement Smith
Mr. & Mrs. P. A. Smith
Mr. & Mrs. T. Smith
Mrs. B. M. Smith
Mr. D. H. Smith
Dr. A. J. Smith
Master B. J. Smith
Mr. E. Smith
Miss C. Smith
Mr. C. G. Smith
Mrs. R. W. Smithson
Mr. A. Snook
Mrs. A. Snow
Mr. M. Snuggs
Mr. E. J. Sobey

Mr. P. H. South
Mrs. L. Speers
Mrs. P. Spicer
Mrs. E. J. Spridgen
Mr. N. P. Spring
Mrs. S. A. Staley
Lt. Col. & Mrs. E. I. Stanford
Mrs. J. G. Staveley
St. Cuthman's School
Mr. W. Steadman
Mr. N. M. Steady
Mrs. P. Stear
Dr. G. A. Steele
Mr. N. H. & Miss K. J. Stennett
Miss E. Stephen
Mr. K. Stephenson
Sir Jeffery Sterling, CBE
Mrs. J. H. Stevens
Mr. C. K. M. Stewart
Mr. & Mrs. C. Stewart
Mr. & Mrs. J. H. Stewart
Mr. L. L. Stiff
Mr. & Mrs. M. G. A. Stocken
Mrs. S. Stokes
Miss L. R. Stoner
Master R. Stott & Mrs. T. Harsley
Mr. G. M. Strachan
Mrs. C. B. Strang Steel
Mrs. M. R. Stratford
Mrs. A. C. Streatfield
Mr. W. H. Strickland
Mr. D. Strutt
Master P. Studholme
Mr. & Mrs. P. Sullivan
Mr. M. M. Sunderland
Mrs. P. J. Swain
Mrs. G. Swanton & Miss S. Read
Mrs. J. R. Sweet
Dr. J. B. Sweet
Mr. J. Swiers
Mrs. J. M. Syddall
Miss H. Syme

T

Mrs. P. A. V. Tanswell
Mr. & Mrs. N. Taplin
Mrs. J. Tasker
Mrs. J. A. Tate
Mr. G. M. Tattersall
Mr. J. S. Taylor
Mrs. H. S. M. Taylor
Mrs. R. A. Taylor
Mrs. A. Taylor
Mrs. S. Taylor
Mr. S. Taylor
Mrs. J. Taylor
Mr. S. V. Taylor
Mr. & Mrs. S. C. S. Taylor
Mr. & Mrs. M. F. Taylor
Miss R. J. Taylor
Messrs. G. & M. Taylor and family
Mrs. S. E. Tee
Mrs. D. J. Terry
Mrs. M. E. Terry
Mr. R. Tetley
Mrs. J. R. Thistlethwayte
Mrs. G. M. P. Thomas
Mrs. J. B. Thomas

Miss M. J. Thomas
Mr. & Mrs. P. Thomas
Mrs. B. Thompson
Mrs. S. M. Thompson
Mrs. R. M. Thompson
Mrs. M. R. P. Thorburn
Mr. J. Thorley
Miss M. Thorley
Thorngrove Centre, The Manager
Mr. & Mrs. J. R. Thorpe
Mrs. G. Thurland
Messrs. Tickle & Warner
Mrs. S. Tilly
Miss M. Tinniswood
Lady Nesta Tirard
Mrs. J. E. G. Todd
Mr. & Mrs. D. F. Tofield
Mr. M. Tomlin
Mr. G. Tosdevine
Mr. & Miss L. Tovey
Miss A. Towell
Messrs. Tracy & Flavey
Mr. & Mrs. P. F. Treacher
Mrs. L. Truelsen
Messrs. M. & L. Trumper
Miss H. Truran
Mr. & Mrs. Tuck
Mr. E. R. Tucker
Mrs. S. Tucker
Mr. O. Tucker
Mr. & Mrs. D. E. Tuffney
Ms. J. M. Turley
Mrs. E. V. Turner
Mr. B. Turner
Mr. & Mrs. G. Turner
Mr. & Mrs. J. E. Turner
Dr. & Mrs. D. Tweedie
Mrs. H. D. Tyson

U

Mr. & Mrs. I. Udale
Miss C. A. Uglow
Mrs. C. M. Unwin
Mr. W. A. Upton
Mrs. D. O. Uridge
Mrs. C. Urquhart

V

Mr. & Mrs. A. W. E. Valender
Mr. & Mrs. W. Valkenburg
Mr. A. A. Van-Suchtelen
Mrs. G. E. Veitch
Mr. J. Venema
Mr. R. Verity
Mr. & Mrs. R. B. Vernon
Mrs. V. J. N. Vernon-Smith
Mrs. S. Vickers
Countess P. H. de Villegas
Mr. M. Vincent
Mr. & Mrs. R. W. Vincent
Herr J. W. A. von Heimendahl

Mr. A. J. Waddington
Mr. & Mrs. Waddington
Mrs. C. E. Wakeford
Mr. M. Wakelin
Waldershare Park Farms Ltd.
Mrs. J. A. Waldron

Mr. & Mrs. A. C. Wales
Mr. R. A. Walker
Mr. B. Walker
Dr. P. R. Walker
Mrs. M. S. D. Walker
Mr. & Mrs. A. Wallace
Mrs. G. Wallace
The Hon. R. Walpole
Mrs. G. W. Walter
Mr. & Mrs. T. R. Walton
Miss N. Ward
Mr. D. I. Ward
Mr. R. M. Ward
Mr. T. Warren
Mrs. P. A. Warwick
Wath Urban Farm
Mr. & Miss Watson
Mrs. C. C. Webb
Mr. J. Webb
Mr. & Mrs. K. G. L. Webb
Mrs. B. H. Webster
Mr. W. Weck
Duke of Wellington Farms
Mr. P. L. Wells
Mr. J. T. Wenham
Mr. B. S. Wessely
Mr. D. A. Wessely
Mrs. B. Westgate
Mr. J. Weston
Weston Park Enterprises Ltd.
Miss A. W. Wheatcroft
Mrs. M. V. B. Wheatcroft
Mrs. H. E. Wheeler
Mrs. A. Whitaker
Mr. F. E. White
Mrs. A. White
Mr. E. C. Whitehead
Mr. W. E. Whitehead

Master R. Whittingham
Mr. D. Whittington
Mr. A. L. Whyte
Mr. G. S. Whyte
Mr. J. A. E. Wick
Mrs. J. J. Wightman
Mr. D. C. Wilcock
Mrs. P. G. Wilkins
Dr. D. J. Wilkinson
Mr. D. Wilkinson
Mrs. J. M. Williams
Mrs. D. V. Williams
Mr. R. P. Williams
Miss E. W. Williams
Mr. T. W. Williams
Mr. & Mrs. S. K. Willis
Mr. & Mrs. J. R. Willis
Mrs. C. Willoughby
Mrs. R. Willows
Mrs. S. Wilmot
Mr. A. M. Wilson
Mrs. J. M. Wilson
Mrs. M. E. Wilson
Mr. & Mrs. G. H. Wilson
Mr. M. J. S. Wilson
Mr. R. J. Wilson
Mrs. H. F. Wilson
Mr. T. P. Winder
Windlestone Hall Residential School
Miss S. Wise
Mrs. J. Wood
Messrs. L. & R. G. Wood
Mr. & Mrs. P. J. R. Wood
Mr. D. Wood
Mr. & Mrs. R. Wood
Mr. & Mrs. B. Wood
Messrs. Wood & Hainsworth
Woodlands Estate

Mr. C. Woods
Mr. & Mrs. J. Woods
Mr. & Mrs. C. Woolf
Mrs. M. L. Woolley
Mrs. L. Woolnough
Mr. & Mrs. D. C. Woosnam
Mrs. V. N. Worrall
Mr. G. O. Worsley
Mr. & Mrs. B. Worsley
Mrs. R. Worth
Brig. A. R. Worthington
Mrs. B. Worthington
Mr. & Mrs. M. Wray
Dr. M. Wright
Miss M. Wright
Mrs. M. J. Wright
Messrs. S. C. & E. C. Wright

Y
Miss J. E. Yardley
Mrs. F. Yates
Mr. G. A. Yates
Mrs. C. Yates
Mr. D. Yates
Mrs. R. M. Yonge
York Livestock Centre
Mr. John Young
Miss V. Young & Miss E. Hemingway
Mrs. A. Young
Miss G. M. Young
Mr. C. R. Young
Mrs. J. A. Younger
Mrs. C. Youngs
Mrs. E. N. Youngs-Dunnett

Z
The Marchioness of Zetland
Mr. J. Zwetsloot

Note of Illustrations

Page No. *Plate No.*

8 — I — Copyright Christies, London. 6th July 1976. Sale. Authenticity verified by thermoluminescence test, Research Laboratory for Archaeology, Oxford. No. 281b 29, 9th April 1976.

Note: A recumbent spotted ram illustrated in 'Antiquities — Geneva' Plate 44 of 5.5.1979 has two particularly fine double curled horns. Dated between 575-550 B.C.

10 — II — Copyright P. E. Newberry, '*El-Bersheh*', I, Pl. XXV. Line drawing from a wall painting in the 2nd tomb of Djehutyhotep at El-Bersheh; signed 'C. G.' so likely to have been engraved by Claude Ferdinand Gaillard 1834-1887. Bryan's Dictionary of Painters and Engravers notes that 'His style both with paint-brush and burin, was a marvel of accurate minuteness'.

13 — III — Copyright Mr. Ernest Erickson of New York, U.S.A. On loan to the Museum of Far Eastern Antiquities, Stockholm, Sweden. The inscription, added later, reads:- Wu Hsing Ch'ien Hsuan Shun-chu, translated is Ch'ien Hsuan Shun-chu, from Wu-hsing. This painting has been attributed to Ch'ien Hsuan but is not by his hand though most probably executed during the 14th Century.

14 — IV — Copyright Christies, London. 15th May 1978. Sale. Detail from 21″ × 33¾″ (53cm × 86cm) picture.

15 — V — Copyright Dr. H. Epstein, from "*Domestic Animals of China*", published by Commonwealth Agricultural Bureaux International, 1969.

16 — VI — Copyright Kate de Rothschild. Private Collection, U.S.A. This drawing, using bodycolour on vellum, is entitled 'Study of Man carrying a Paper with the Motto "Omnia mea mecum porto" in a Landscape with animals'. The subject may be Diogenes who left his wordly goods behind when he went to live in a cave wearing only a large cloak. 'I carry all I possess with me' implies that he only takes what he wears.

17 — VII — Copyright The Lady Juliet de Chair.

18 — VIII — Copyright Pinacoteca Ambrosiana, Milan; the home town of the artist.

18 — IX — Copyright William Youatt. '*Sheep, Their Breeds, Management and Diseases*', 1837, p. 141. M. Ryder.

23 — X — Copyright Author. James Stewart, Serjeant Painter to King George III in 1764. Engraved by William H. Lizars 1788-1859, Scottish painter and engraver.

24 — XI — GISBURN PARK. Copyright Guildhall Library, London. From 'History & Antiquities of The Deanery of Craven. T. D. Whitaker. Republished 1973. Mid 18th Century.

25 — XII — Copyright Christies, London. 7th July 1988. Sale. 45″ × 60″ (114cm × 153cm).

25 — XIII — Copyright Pergamon Museum, East Berlin. Room 12, Case 37.

25 — XIV — Photographed by the late Professor J. A. Dudgeon, CBE., M.C., 1984, Jordan.

26 — XV — Copyright the Smithsonian Museum, Washington, U.S.A.

26 — XVI — Copyright, collection of National Palace Museum, Taiwan, Republic of China. Detail from 'Parting of Su Wu and Li Ling' by Chou Wen-Chüh, Five dynasties (906-960).

27 — XVII — Photographed by Author's son, Hon. Charles Low, 1976, Peking, China.

27 — XVIII — Copyright The Islamic Museum of Berlin, East Germany. The original miniature 7¼″ × 4½″ is from an Album collected in 1767 by the 26 year old Swiss, Antoine Louis Henri de Polier, who served as a Major in the British Army under Lord Clive in India. In 1882 the Album was bought by the Prussian State when the Hamilton Collection was auctioned in London.

28 — XIX — Copyright The Maharaja Sawai Man Singh II Museum, City Palace, Jaipur. On loan to The Metropolitan Museum of Art, New York, U.S.A.

28 — XX — Copyright The Earl of Mansfield, Scone Palace, Perthshire, Scotland.

33 — XXI — Photographed by Susan Catch. *Also*
100 — L — *both inside cover photographs, 1989.*

41 — XXII — BLAKESLEY HALL. Private Collection 1880.

41 — XXIII — Property of Ex J.S.S. Founder Member 1931/32.

43 — XXIV — BULSTRODE. Copyright Newport Borough Libraries 1768.

46- — XXV- — CANON'S ASHBY. Copyright The
47 — XXVI — Trustees of the late Mrs. C. Dryden. By kind permission of Northamptonshire Record Office Ref. D. (G.A.) 506.

57 — XXVII — GRANGE PARK. Copyright Tadman. British Museum Newspaper Library. 'The Field' 23rd July 1910.

50 — XXVIII — INGLEBOROUGH. Copyright by kind permission of the Northamptonshire Record Office. Ref. D (C.A.) 506.

Page No.	Plate No.	
67	XXIX	MILTON. Copyright Sport & General. British Museum Newspaper Library, Colindale. "Farmer & Stockbreeder" July 1910.
68	XXX-XXXI	MONTREAL. Copyright A. C. Cooper, London. From: Hasted's 'History of Kent' 1774.
73	XXXII	RYCOTE PARK. Reproduced from Robert Plot's 'History of Oxfordshire'. 1677.
75	XXXIII	SCOTLAND LODGE. Copyright John Llewelyn Jones, Clevedon, Avon. 1964.
76	XXXIV	SHALSTONE MANOR. Photograph the property of G. P. Purefoy. J.S.S No. 9. c.1900.
77	XXXV XXXVI XXXVII	SHANBALLY CASTLE. Photographs the property of Mrs. R. Beecher. J.S.S. No. 898. 1932.
80	XXXVIII	TABLEY PARK. a) Tabley Old Hall. Copyright Victoria University of Manchester, The Tabley Collection 1760. Neg. No. B88/1010 P.S. The property of Courtauld Insitute of Art.
81	XXXIX	b) c) Two Lithographs. Copyright Victoria University of Manchester, The Tabley Collection 1822.

Page No.	Plate No.	
82	XL	d) 4) Negatives, property of the author. c.1934.
85	XLI	TATTON PARK. Copyright John Rylands University Library of Manchester. Ref. Egerton of Tatton, 2/3/1408 233/89.
89 90	XLII XLIII	WENTWORTH WOODHOUSE. Sheffield City Archives. Ref. WWM.A.1327x2. WWM 1495 (p. 13). Copyright 'Olive, Countess Fitzwilliam's Wentworth Settlement Trustees and the Director.'
97	XLIV	Rosa Bonheur. Copyright 'Trustees of the Wallace Collection'.
97	XLV	James Ward, R.A. Private Collection by kindness of Ex J.S.S. Member.
98	XLVI	BILTON HALL. Private Collection via Leger Galleries. London c.1792.
98	XLVII	CHARLCOTE PARK. Photographed by M. de Pickard 1989.
99	XLVIII	CHATSWORTH. Photographed by British Wool Marketing Board c.1981.
99	XLIX	e) Map, hand drawn by J.S.S. No. 581 from 6" to mile Townland survey of 1841 of Queen's County, Ireland.
100	LI	Private Collection: B. Harford.